Dendrobiums

an introduction to the species in cultivation

Professor E.A. Schelpe, D. Phil. (Oxon.)
Curator of the Bolus Herbarium and Senior Lecturer in Plant Taxonomy, University of Cape Town

Carmen Coll

Sheffield Orchid Congress
April 1996.
B. Farell.

Dendrobiums

an introduction to the species in cultivation

Sybella Schelpe and Joyce Stewart

Orchid Sundries Ltd.
Stour Provost, Dorset

Front cover photograph: *D. draconis.*

Back cover photograph: *D. falconeri.*

Published in 1990 by Orchid Sundries Ltd.,
New Gate Farm, Stour Provost,
Gillingham, Dorset SB8 5LT

Reprinted 1995

ISBN 1 873 03500 4

Typeset in 11 on 12pt Baskerville.

Printed in Great Britain by
Blackmore Press
Shaftesbury, Dorset.

Contents

Dedication

This book is dedicated to the memory of Ted Schelpe who had a deep and lifelong interest in all aspects of orchidology.

Foreword

Ted Schelpe started to grow orchids as a schoolboy in Durban, with the encouragement of his mother. Dendrobiums were his first love. While he was a postgraduate student at Oxford, he went as botanist on an expedition to the Himalaya. He saw dendrobiums in the forests on the lower slopes and collected his first tropical orchids. Over the years, Ted visited India, Nepal, Thailand, Malaysia, Hong Kong, New Guinea and Australia to study the different species in the wild. He corresponded with other botanists, including Eric Holttum, Victor Summerhayes, Peter Hunt and Phillip Cribb at Kew, Leslie Garay at Harvard, Rapee Sagarik in Bangkok, Tony Lamb in Sabah, Andree Millar at Lae and Gunnar Seidenfaden in Denmark, in trying to sort out the taxonomy and nomenclature in some of the sections of *Dendrobium*. Some of the results of these studies were published in the *'South African Orchid Journal'* and in *'The Orchid Digest'*.

For many years Ted grew *Dendrobium* species in his garden and greenhouses in Cape Town. With Louis Vogelpoel he began to compile a photographic record of the species in cultivation, in his own and other collections. By the time of his early death in 1985, he had often talked to us about the illustrated book he wanted to write for orchid lovers, about the dendrobiums that they could grow.

We have tried to write that book as we believe Ted would have wished us to do. His notes, published papers, photographs and records have all been invaluable to us. We have also drawn on our own experiences both in the wild and in cultivation. Sybella has cared for the Schelpe collection and added to it since 1985. She has selected the photographs and commissioned the artist, Fay Anderson, to paint *Dendrobium schuetzei* from the plant at 'Westfield'. Joyce has grown most of the species in this book, first in Nairobi, then Pietermaritzburg and now in Dorset, and she has written the text. In fact *Dendrobium densiflorum* was the first cultivated orchid she ever bought, in 1964. That plant is still doing well and flowers every spring, despite several major moves across the world. Furthermore, it has been divided many times, and divisions of it have started several young orchid growers in this fascinating hobby.

This is not the first book on dendrobiums and their cultivation, and it certainly will not be the last. However, we believe that it will be a useful introduction for many enthusiasts who are becoming interested in growing orchids and want to find out more about these floriferous plants. We hope that it will help them to understand the botany of this huge genus and lead them to new species that they can grow. Above all we hope that it will help them to grow and flower their plants well because that is what Ted always wanted to encourage people to do.

Thanks

We wish to record our thanks to all the people who have helped us in producing this book. We especially want to thank Jean Dryden for her unstinting help with the orchid plants at 'Westfield' and for her assistance in assembling and cataloguing the colour transparencies. We also thank Fay Anderson for the time and trouble she spent to produce the beautiful watercolour of *Dendrobium schuetzei*. We are extremely grateful to Carmen Coll (for the frontispiece), Louis Vogelpoel, Donald Stewart, and Phillip Cribb for their photographs, and to the Director, Royal Botanic Gardens, Kew who has lent some transparencies given to Kew by various photographers, whom we have acknowledged on the relevant pages, to make this book complete. Some photographs were taken by Jean Dryden and Joyce Stewart and all the others by Ted Schelpe. Finally, a heartfelt expression of thanks to our publishers and printer for making this book a reality.

Sybella Schelpe
Westfield
Lemon Lane
Newlands
Cape 7700
South Africa

Joyce Stewart
The Croft
Burt's Lane, Mannington
Wimborne
Dorset BH21 7JX
England

Introduction

The genus *Dendrobium* is one of the largest in the orchid family. The precise number of species it contains can only be guessed at. Many botanists today would say that there are at least 1,000; others would guess that there are more than 1,400. In the Old World — from India eastwards to Japan and south to Australia, New Zealand and Fiji — it is rivalled only by the genus *Bulbophyllum*, which approaches it in size but cannot do so in the beauty of the flowers or the number of species of horticultural merit. In the New World, *Epidendrum* is a large genus with colourful flowers, but there are many more species in the relatively unstudied *Pleurothallis*.

Most *Dendrobium* plants are epiphytes, but others have taken to life on rocks and cliffs with equal success. Rather few are terrestrial plants. There are some which grow very well in grasslands at high altitudes, and others which have proved to be good colonisers of roadsides in their tropical habitats.

There is a tremendous diversity of plant habit and size within the genus. There are plants with dwarf pseudobulbs growing close together in tufts only 1 cm or so high, and there are others with immense cane-like stems of more than 3 m. Some have very slender, wiry stems, often pendent. Others are elegantly slender, curved or swollen, while yet others are robust and erect, tall or short.

Many species of *Dendrobium* have short-lived leaves, described as deciduous. They last for a few months on each newly developing growth but are shed as soon as the dry season approaches. Others have tougher leaves that last for many years, even throughout the life of the plant. They vary in size from tiny to very large. In colour almost every shade of green is represented. Some are thick, fleshy and almost succulent with curious shapes. A few are hairy. In such a large genus the diversity of leaf form is very great.

There is also great variety in the flower arrangement. In a few plants the flowers are solitary but more often they are arranged in inflorescences, many together, and many inflorescences may be carried by a plant at any one flowering season. It is the floriferousness of plants in the wild, and in good conditions under cultivation, which is the major part of the attraction of dendrobiums.

Flower size and colour are extremely varied too. The smallest flowers are only a few millimetres across and may have rather dull colours or very bright, almost incandescent ones. The largest flowers are 10 cm or more in diameter. Some of the largest ones are the brightest, often with several contrasting colours within a single flower making it very spectacular. Almost every colour can be found in this one genus, except perhaps a real blue. The flowers vary between tough and waxy, lasting in perfection for many months on the plant, and delicately transparent, some of them lasting for less than a day.

Despite this great diversity, the flowers of all the species possess a similarity of structure which makes them instantly recognisable and unites them in this single huge genus. They are always symmetrical, with three, more or less equal sepals forming the frame against which the rather different petals and lip are displayed. The column is extended below its point of attachment to the ovary into a structure known as the column foot. The base of the lip is attached to this foot and often the lateral sepals are adnate to it so that a kind of 'mentum', or chin, is formed which may even be extended into a conspicuous spur. Hidden under the anther cap at the apex of the column are four pollinia, each oval or oblong, bright yellow and rather waxy, and lacking any kind of stalk or gland to aid the pollinator.

This brief description fits all members of the genus but it does not reveal the tremendously varied flowers which can be found among its constituent species. Some of that variety, beauty and interest will be revealed in the following pages.

Because of the great variety, within the apparent similarity in *Dendrobium*, botanists have found it convenient to divide the genus into sections, each of which can be recognised by some distinctive character or peculiarity which is easily noticed. Dr. John Lindley produced the first attempt at a sectional classification in *Dendrobium* with ten different sections. Kraenzlin produced a monograph of the whole genus in 1910, but the system he proposed has been much criticised. Schlechter's system, proposed in his treatment of the New Guinea orchids in 1914, has found more favour, though perhaps the number of different sections he proposed is excessive. Brieger's proposals to split the genus up into a number of smaller genera similar to Schlechter's sections has not found favour with other botanists. Most botanists who have studied *Dendrobium* recently, including Holttum, Seidenfaden, Schelpe, Cribb and Woods, have followed Schlechter's sectional arrangement, with modifications, and in Chapter 3 we present a brief summary of Schelpe's use of it in his paper published in the *'South African Orchid Journal'* in 1985.

The greater part of this book is devoted to the description and illustration of the species that are commonly grown, or could be grown by enthusiasts. Some historical and geographical information is included. The latter is often particularly useful to growers, giving clues as to the best treatment of plants to aid the maximum growth and production of flowers. Similar species are presented together in their sections as an aid to the identification of unknown plants. We hope that this presentation of the dendrobiums in cultivation, showing the species in their sectional relationships, will bring more understanding and interest to the lovers of these popular and widely grown orchids.

Chapter 1
Dendrobiums and their Habitats

The name *Dendrobium* is made up of two Greek words, *'dendron'* — tree and *'bios'* — life, apparently referring to the epiphytic habit of most of the species. It was a Swedish botanist, Olof Swartz, who published a synopsis of the orchids known to him, in 1800, in which several new genera were established, including *Dendrobium*. At that time there were 9 species.

CHARACTERISTICS OF THE PLANT

The plants have a sympodial growth habit. Each season's growth emerges from a node at or near the base of the preceding one. Sometimes a horizontal stem or rhizome, from which the upright stems arise, can be clearly seen, but often it is rather indistinguishable. Nevertheless, each season's new growth is of limited duration, producing leaves and flowers in due course, sometimes over many years, and gradually being superseded by other growths. It is safe to say that, barring natural disasters in the wild, a *Dendrobium* plant will never die. It simply goes on growing, gradually moving across the space of the available substratum.

Usually the season's new growths are so close to each other that the plant has a tufted habit. A mass of roots emerges from the base of each stem and clings tenaciously to the rock or bark, holding the plant in place. Often the roots are rather slender, and they are covered with an absorbent layer of velamen so that they can retain moisture even when conditions become quite dry.

The upright or pendulous stems are extremely variable. Some are narrowly cylindrical or wiry, others are swollen to form distinctive pseudobulbs. Many are fleshy or slightly swollen throughout their length so that they resemble a cane. All are jointed, made up of several successive internodes between the nodes where the leaves are attached, either directly or through an intermediate sheathing base. In the latter case, the internodes are completely encased in the greyish white or hairy leaf sheaths. Many stems become furrowed or wrinkled with age, or change colour as they mature.

The leaves are always simple, undivided, but vary greatly in shape, from narrow and grass-like to wide and fleshy or succulent. They are always arranged alternately in two ranks along the stem. In many species the leaves last only a few months or weeks and are soon deciduous. Others are biennial in their duration, while those that are attached only to the apex of the stems are usually more persistent.

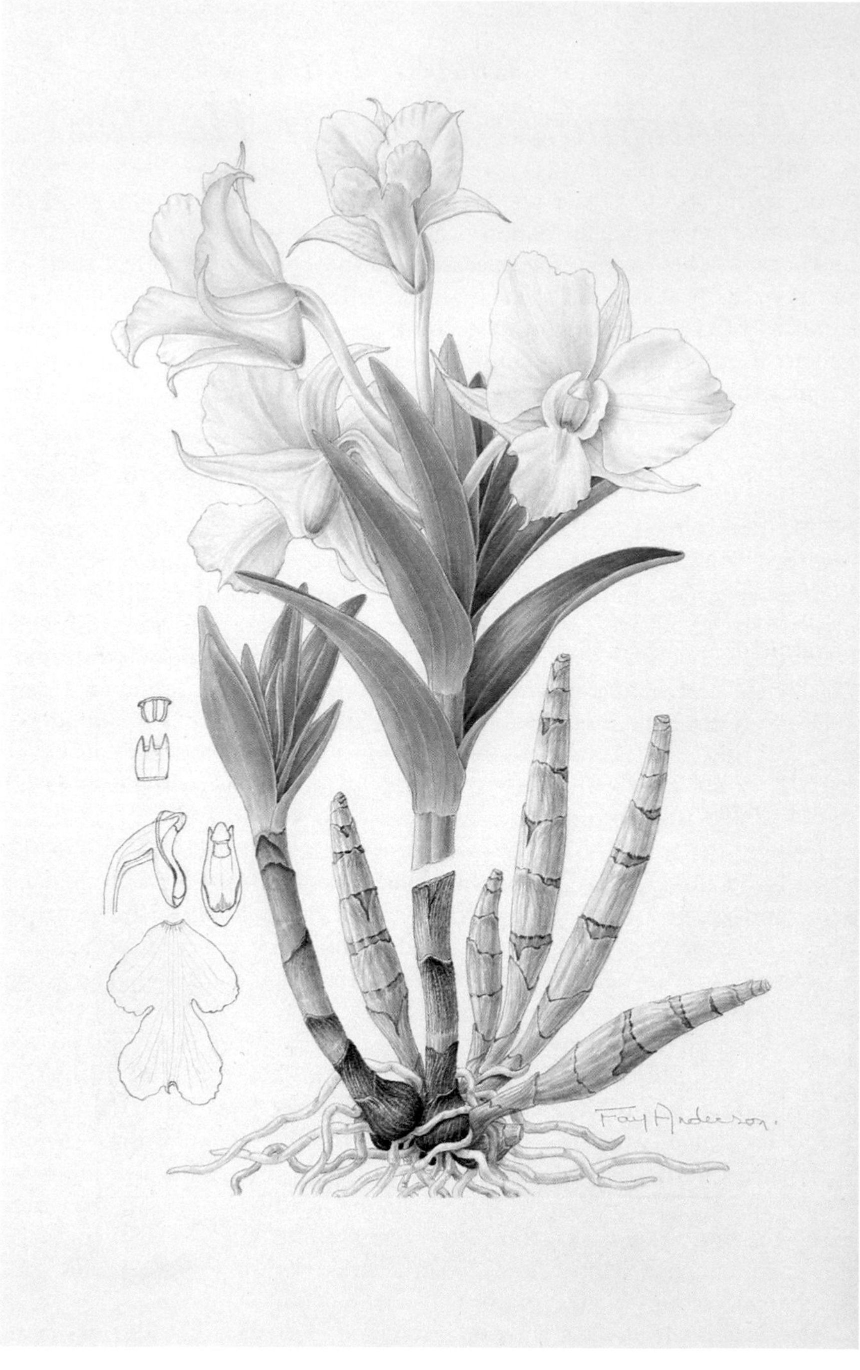

Dendrobium schuetzei, flowering plant with old pseudobulbs on the right and the newest growth on the left. The dissections at the lower left show (bottom), the shape of the lip; (centre), side and lower surface views of the column; (above), upper view of part of the column and two pollinia adhering to the detached anther cap. *Fay Anderson*

The inflorescence is lateral but may only grow from the uppermost nodes and appear terminal. In many of the deciduous species the flowers are solitary or in small groups of 2-4. They appear from the nodes of the stem on the side opposite to which the leaf had been. In the evergreen species, or those in which the leaves are persistent for several seasons, the flowers are borne in elongated racemes, usually from the nodes among or just below the leaves and for several years in succession.

The characters of the flowers are remarkably consistent and can be summarised as follows

— The **sepals** are more or less equal. The dorsal sepal is free. The lateral sepals are adnate to the foot of the column and form a **mentum** between it and the base of the lip. In some species the mentum is extended into a spur.
— The **petals** are usually the same length as the sepals, somtimes longer, often much broader, rarely narrower.
— The **lip** is more or less contracted at the base into a claw, next to or actually joined to the foot of the column.
— The **column** is extended below the point of its attachment to the ovary into a kind of foot. The part of the column above the point of attachment, extending forward into the flower, is very short.
— The moveable **anther cap** is located at the apex of the column and it conceals the 4 **pollinia** which lie parallel to one another. They are waxy in texture and oval or oblong.
— The **capsule** is rounded or ovoid, sometimes winged, rarely elongated.

DISTRIBUTION

Dendrobiums are distributed over a very wide area of the Old World. Their greatest density is in the Himalayan region, the Malay archipelago, New Guinea, Australia and the islands of the western Pacific. There are also outliers in Sri Lanka and peninsular India, Japan, Taiwan, New Zealand and the Society Islands. Within this vast area, however, there are rather few species that are widespread and some are restricted to a very narrow range. Most of the species are epiphytes and very few, if any, can be described as frost-tolerant. They are therefore truly tropical orchids, even though many can withstand quite low temperatures for part of the year. Temperature and humidity are the limiting factors where space is available.

CLIMATE

The climate of the area where dendrobiums occur is characterised by a high average temperature accompanied by abundant moisture for much of the year. At higher elevations in the mountains, and further south in Australia, there are modifications in both respects.

In the lower Himalayan region the temperature ranges from 27-33°C and even higher in some of the valleys in June. In December, however, it is at least 6-9°C lower. The humidity of the atmosphere during the greater part of the year is at or near saturation point, because of the incidence of heavy rain. The precipitation increases greatly towards the hills where 600 inches have been recorded in a year and a fall of 250 inches is not unkown in one month during August. This tremendous amount is quite local and only a few miles away there may be less than half.

In many parts of Assam, the rainfall is very considerable. The wettest months are June to September, with the heaviest falls occurring in July. From the middle of October to near the end of February the season is rainless and there is a decided 'rest' for all the vegetation. The day temperatures in the area from March to September range from 24-33°C while the night temperature is usually 5-6°C lower. In the dry season the day temperature is 5-8°C lower than during the rains while the lowest night temperatures are only 7-10°C.

Dendrobiums are abundant in these districts, growing chiefly on trees where they are exposed to plenty of fresh air.

In Burma and Thailand the climate is somewhat similar. Heavy rain falls during the summer months when temperatures are highest and the atmosphere is steamy. On ascending the mountains, however, a distinct change is noticed. Even at 500 m there is a distinct fall in temperature at night, to below 10°C just before sunrise. Because of the mountains, there is frequent mist and cloud so that the dry season is much shorter than in India, from December to the middle of March. But the drought is very noticeable, with the trees losing their leaves and all herbaceous vegetation becoming shrivelled and dry, and temperatures during the day may rise to 45°C.

Many *nobile*-type and *Callista* dendrobiums grow in these kinds of conditions.

In the Malaysian countries and southwards to New Guinea, what might be termed the equatorial region, the most characteristic feature of the climate is that it is much more equable by day and night. The highest temperatures are seldom much more than 33°C, but they do not fall below 23°C at night. Often the daily range of temperature is little more than 5°C. For a large part of the year the air is nearly saturated with moisture and there are frequent and copious falls of dew and rain despite the warmth. During the 'wet' season it is rare to have more than a few days without sunshine and during the 'dry' season there are frequent showers. At higher altitudes the temperatures are much modified and the rainfall is also modified by local topography. Parts of the Borneo and New Guinea mountains can be quite cold.

Eastern Australia is partly tropical and partly temperate, the rainfall amount is much more restricted and becomes less further south. It also becomes seasonal, though in the mountains there is cloud and fog to supplement it.

This brief review of some of the climatic conditions that prevail in the parts of the world where dendrobiums grow has been presented to demonstrate how varied the conditions they experience can be. Perhaps the two things that are most important for the grower of *Dendrobium* species to try to discover, in order to grow plants well, are the source country and altitudinal range in which every species of interest grows. This information can tell you a great deal about the growing requirements of a new plant. It is probably not possible to emulate the wild conditions exactly. That would be impossible in the limitations of a glass structure in temperate climates. But it should be possible to provide conditions in which all the species can grow. Making an artificial environment which most nearly resembles the wild conditions offers the best chance of success.

D. nobile in a tropical garden
Joyce Stewart

Chapter 2
Cultivation

Dendrobiums are best grown in shade houses in tropical countries and in glass or plastic 'greenhouses' in temperate regions. The exact structure of these buildings is not important, but they should be oriented so that the maximum amount of light is available to the plants they contain during the winter months. Ideally, a suitable greenhouse will be subdivided, so that several different sets of conditions, particularly night temperatures, can be provided. Alternatively, and if space is available, a number of separate structures can be utilised. If only one house is possible, there is no difficulty in arranging several different kinds of conditions within it, by means of blinds or the positioning of other plants. There is always a big difference in humidity and temperature between the floor area and just below the roof glass.

There are four important features to consider in providing the right environment for dendrobiums to flourish in a greenhouse. They are

— moisture, amount and frequency
— temperature, both by night and day
— light, especially during the winter and, conversely, shade in the summer months and
— fresh air.

WATERING, DAMPING DOWN AND FEEDING

We have indicated in the text relating to many of the species how the frequency and amount of watering must depend on the season of the year and the condition of the plants. Dormant or 'resting' plants do not need watering but they do need to be in a humid atmosphere, or to have some dampness around their roots in order to prevent excessive shrivelling of the stems or pseudobulbs. When the new growths begin to develop roots, watering must be carefully increased until it is supplied daily in liberal amounts. This continues until the stem finally completes its growth and the last leaf matures. Then water is gradually reduced until the plants are at rest again.

Damping down by spraying on the staging and floor increases the humidity surrounding the plants and also lowers the temperature. It is beneficial several times a day during the summer months, especially in the evening so that the humidity is high at night. During the winter it can be reduced to once or twice daily and not at all on rainy or overcast days.

Feeding the plants with a very dilute liquid fertiliser is very beneficial while they are actively growing. Every other watering is not too frequent. When temperatures are high, food can be included in every application of water.

TEMPERATURES

Some species of *Dendrobium* require very little extra heat beyond what is available from the sun shining through glass. But most require some artificial heating at night, not only during the winter but also during the spring months when new growths are beginning. In the text describing the requirements of individual species, we have used the terms 'warm', 'intermediate' and 'cool' as they are used by many orchid growers to describe minimum night temperatures during the winter, viz.

warm, 15-18°C
intermediate, 12-13°C
cool 10°C

A daytime rise of at least 5°C should be ensured throughout the year and preferably at least 10-15°C in summer.

Excessive temperatures are more often a problem in small greenhouses than large ones, especially in summer. Careful attention to ventilation and shading are necessary, as temperatures which are too high can cause stunted growth and scorched foliage. Nevertheless, shading should not be so heavy that it seriously reduces the light.

LIGHT

In the northern hemisphere, no shading is required from the middle of October to the middle of March. This period can often be lengthened by two weeks at either end of the season. Complete shading is required for 6-7 hours a day from June to August, when the days are hot and sunny, but can be dispensed with on dull days. In the remaining months, the duration of shading can be increased or diminished according to season and local weather conditions.

In the southern hemisphere the seasons are simply reversed.

FRESH AIR

We cannot emphasise too strongly that ventilation and air movement are vital for the healthy growth of the plants and the maintenance of a good leaf temperature. Ventilators in the roof and sides of the greenhouse are invaluable. Where winter temperatures are low it is better to make use of interior electric fans and avoid opening the windows to lose warmth or humidity or both. Often growers are tempted to have very little air movement so that the plants dry out more slowly, but this is a very unnatural situation. It is much better to water and damp down frequently and have a gale blowing through the greenhouse. That is what happens in nature.

POTTING

Many dendrobiums have pendulous stems and look most attractive grown in teak baskets. They also do well in small pots that are hung up from the roof or other form of support. Plastic pots with basket-like construction are ideal for many species. Some of the smaller ones are best mounted directly on to slabs of cork oak bark or tree fern fibre. They must be tied on firmly as they take time to get established and a loose plant will never grow.

Upright plants do best in pots of a well drained compost mix based on bark or charcoal. The base of the plant should stand at or above the rim of the pot to facilitate good drainage. Many dendrobiums have fine roots, and not too many of them, so small pots are usually required. This means the plants will require some form of support until they become established.

The best time to repot, or change the compost mix in a basket, is when the new growths are just starting, preferably before they have begun to produce their brittle roots. This usually means dendrobiums should be repotted soon after flowering. Thus repotting can be spread over the year, to fit in with the growth and flowering pattern of the various species.

PESTS AND DISEASES

Dendrobiums suffer from the same pests as other orchids if they are grown inside a greenhouse. Red spider, mealy bug and scale insects are the worst offenders. They can be kept in check with several acaricides and insecticides and if dealt with as soon as they are noticed will rarely become harmful if growing conditions are right. Slugs and snails are also a nuisance when new growths or flower buds are present. Nocturnal vigilance, with a torch, and a means of disposing of them are the best means of defence and, at times, rewarding. Mice occasionally invade greenhouses and must be deterred.

Several bacterial and fungal diseases have been recorded on dendrobiums and may need rapid attention to prevent their spread. The provision of adequate air movement and the use of Physan as a general greenhouse and plant disinfectant will reduce their incidence.

Virus diseases are not a great problem with orchids imported from the wild but can be spread from other infected plants in collections. Great care should be taken when repotting, and with cutting tools, that plant sap from a possibly infected plant is not spread to others.

PROPAGATION

Dendrobium species are easily raised from seeds on any of the standard media. Owners of rare and unusual specimens are urgently requested to self-pollinate or cross their plants and make seeds available to those who can germinate them and produce seedlings.

Meristem and other tissue culture techniques have also been used with great success with some of the cultivated dendrobiums, especially in Hawaii and southeast Asia. These have the advantage that precisely similar progeny are usually obtained from the parent plant. However, this can also be a disadvantage, in that the genetic diversity that is preserved in cultivated plants by this technique can be greatly reduced.

Many species of *Dendrobium* produce 'keikis' or small offshoots from the upper nodes. Once these have begun to produce roots they can be detached from the parent plant and established alone in a small container.

Large plants can be divided. Frequently the basal rhizome branches, and plants develop a number of leading growths. When these large plants are unpotted, they may fall apart quite naturally, or they can be carefully separated to form a number of smaller plants for repotting.

Many dendrobiums need pruning when they are repotted. Too many old stems can be unsightly and should be removed from large plants. If they are still firm, the detached stems can be cut into lengths, 10-15 cm long, and laid on some moss or peat in a well shaded and humid place. Within a few weeks, dormant buds at the nodes will begin to form new plants, not on every node, but enough to satisfy most growers who wish to share their plants with others.

SOURCES OF PLANTS

Probably the best means of obtaining *Dendrobium* species, many of which are already in cultivation, is from other enthusiasts. Nurserymen and amateur growers have a surprising variety of plants on their staging, or hung up in their greenhouses, which they are only too delighted to share or sell. Meetings of orchid societies and shows are also a good venue for plant hunting. Duplicates of mature plants or surplus seedlings are often available.

Several specialist nurseries now sell small numbers of seedlings in flasks to appeal to amateurs with small greenhouses. These are an excellent source of interesting species. The thrill of raising plants from a flask is something that every grower should experience.

The days of large importations from the jungles have disappeared. Today, orchid lovers must raise more plants from those already in cultivation or from rarely collected orchid capsules. New nurseries are developing in southeast Asia and several of them are interested in raising native species among the huge quantity of hybrids they are developing for the cut flower market. The amount of work involved in raising orchid seedlings is considerable and specialists who are making rare species available in this way deserve support.

Chapter 3
Classification

The German orchidologist Rudolf Schlechter proposed a very useful subdivision of the genus *Dendrobium* in his massive work on the orchids of New Guinea which was completed in 1914. He divided the genus into four subgenera, and each subgenus into sections.

This subdivision has found a large measure of acceptance among modern botanists, and until someone becomes fully acquainted with the entire genus, and can propose something more workable, it is still in use and found to be very helpful in many herbaria.

Schlechter's work has become known to a wider public since 1982 when the excellent translation by Blaxell, Katz and Simmons became available in English. We have summarised Schlechter's classification for our own use in compiling the present book and reproduce it below.

Key to the subgenera

Leaves without distinct sheaths at the base	*Athecebium*
Leaves borne upon a sheathing base	
Pseudobulbs or stems fleshy	
Pseudobulbs or stems fleshy for the whole length	*Dendrobium*
Pseudobulbs or stems fleshy for 1-3 internodes only	*Rhopalobium*
Stems wiry, dry, always very slender	*Xerobium*

In the following lists of Sections within each subgenus we have modified some of the names to bring them in line with currently acceptable nomenclature. The ones which have examples illustrated and described in this book are shown in bold face. It becomes apparent from this list that our book is, indeed, only an introduction to this fascinating genus.

Subgenus *Athecebium*
Sections *Desmotrichum*
Microphytanthe
Goniobulbon
Diplocaulobium (now treated as a distinct genus)
Bolbidium
Euphlebium
Rhizobium
Sarcopodium (now treated as a distinct genus)
Dendrocoryne
Latouria
Inobulbon
Callista

Subgenus *Dendrobium*
Sections **Dendrobium**
Platycaulon
Pedilonum
Calyptrochilus
Oxyglossum (including Schlechter's *Cuthbertsonia*)
Breviflores (including Schlechter's *Brachyanthe*)
Stachyobium
Fytchianthe
Phalaenanthe
Eleutheroglossum
Spatulata (called *Ceratobium* by Schlechter)
Trachyrhizum
Distichophyllum
Formosae (called *Oxygenianthe* by Schlechter)
Amblyanthus
Kinetochilus

Subgenus *Rhopalobium*
Sections *Rhopalanthe*

Subgenus *Xerobium*
Sections *Aporum*
Oxystophyllum
Grastidium
Dichopus
Eriopexis
Pleianthe
Macrocladium
Dolichocentrum
Conostalix
Monanthos
Herpethophytum

Chapter 4
Section Dendrobium
(formerly known as *Eugenanthe*)

These are the typical dendrobiums, sometimes called the 'soft cane' species. The stems are fleshy and may form distinctly cane-like pseudobulbs or remain slender and pendent. The leaves are arranged alternately along the stems and have tightly sheathing bases, each sheath enclosing the internode of the stem below the point at which the leaf blade is articulated. The leaves remain fresh and green for one or two growing seasons and are then shed. The inflorescences usually arise on the leafless pseudobulbs, but sometimes also among the leaves on mature stems.

The flowers of this section are easily recognised. Sometimes they are borne singly, but more often on short inflorescences. The sepals and petals are similar and much less conspicuous than the lip which is more or less hairy on its inner surface. The lip is entire, and there is a very short mentum at its base.

This section is widespread throughout continental Asia, extending eastwards to Korea, Japan and Taiwan, and southwards to Borneo. For ease of identification we have divided this large section into four informal groups as follows

Groups 1-3

Short, 1-3 flowered inflorescences produced from many nodes along the pseudobulbs

1. Sepals and petals pink, purple, white flushed pink or white tipped with purple or pink
2. Sepals and petals yellow, pale yellow or cream
3. Sepals and petals orange red

Group 4

Usually longer and pendulous inflorescences with 5-15 flowers from the upper nodes of the pseudobulbs, flowers yellow or pinkish yellow

Group 1 Inflorescences with 1-3 flowers at each of several nodes; sepals and petals lilac, pink, purple, white flushed with pink or white tipped with pinkish purple.

Dendrobium moniliforme (L.) Sw.
(Syn. *D. monile* (Thunb.) Kraenzl.
D. japonicum Lindl.)

This species was first described by Olof Swartz in 1799 and has since been selected as the type of the genus. It is a cool-growing orchid distributed through Japan, Korea and Taiwan. Throughout its wide range there is considerable variation among the forms and colours of both the plants and flowers.

In the wild the plants are epiphytic or lithophytic, and the stems grow in dense tufts. They vary between 10 and 40 cm long and although slender they are often somewhat thickened towards the middle. They may be green, purple, brown or yellow, the darker forms bearing darker leaves and some of the paler ones bearing variegated leaves. The leaves are always narrow and 3-5 cm long. The inflorescences arise on the older stems after the leaves have fallen, bearing 1-2 flowers each. The flowers are fragrant, 2-4.5 cm across, but not always opening fully, white or pink, the lip often somewhat greenish yellow and with brown spots towards the base.

D. moniliforme
Louis Vogelpoel

This species grows easily in a greenhouse which is kept cool, particularly in winter. A cool, dry season of several months is necessary to initiate flowering in the spring. It does equally well in a clay or plastic pot or when mounted on a piece of bark. It is often one of the first species to flower in early spring and delightful both for the sudden appearance of its flowers and for their fragrance.

D. nobile var. cooksonianum
Louis Vogelpoel

Dendrobium nobile Lindl.

Although not described until 1830, this species is the most well known of all dendrobiums and one of the most commonly grown in cultivation. Its name is often used to describe this group of plants which are referred to as '*nobile*-type' dendrobiums. It is widespread in the wild and has been collected from many parts of the Himalayan region, in Nepal, Sikkim, Bhutan, northeast India, Burma, southern China, Vietnam, Laos and Thailand. Plants have always been recorded as growing and flowering in full sun at altitudes below 1500 m.

D. nobile var. splendens
E.A. Schelpe

The pseudobulbs grow in tufts and are swollen at the nodes so that they appear jointed, 30-60 cm long. Leaves bright green and usually persistent for two seasons. The flowers rather variable in colour with a lustrous waxy surface, 5-7 cm across, the petals wider than the sepals. The basal area is white or pale pink with a stronger amethyst-purple colour towards the tips, sometimes covering the whole surface. The lip is downy with a rich maroon-purple basal part surrounded by a yellowish white zone.

Often described as a beginner's orchid, this species is very easy to grow in cultivation, but it must be kept dry, and given as much light as possible during the winter, in order to bloom in spring.

Several different varieties have been described and are still in cultivation. The most frequently seen are the var. *virginale*, which is white with a yellowish green centre to the lip, and the var. *cooksonianum* in which the petals resemble the lip, each having a broad, maroon, velvety blotch in the basal half. *Dendrobium nobile*

D. nobile hybrids
Joyce Stewart

has been widely used in hybridising and a large number of hybrids bred by Jiro Yamamoto and others are now available.

Dendrobium linawianum Reichb.f.

Occurs in China, Japan and Taiwan and is rather like a miniature version of *D. nobile*. The purple colouration at the base of the lip forms two large spots, one on each side.

D. linawianum
Louis Vogelpoel

Dendrobium falconeri Hook.

This species was one of many importations to England from India in the middle of the nineteenth century. It was named by Sir William Hooker as a compliment to Dr. Falconer who was Director of the Calcutta Botanic Garden. It flowers in the early summer from its knotty, untidy, pendent stems which cannot really be mistaken for those of any other species. In the wild it has been recorded from Bhutan, northeast India, Burma, Thailand, southwest China and Taiwan, from 1200 to 2300 m above sea level.

Stem branching, slender, pendent, swollen at the nodes which are about 5 cm apart except on the side branches where they are close together and may look like strings of beads. The stems often produce bunches of roots at the nodes. The leaves are small, narrow and short-lived. The

flowers are solitary, 5-7 cm in diameter. The sepals and petals are white, tipped with amethyst purple, the petals wider than the sepals. The ovate lip is sharply pointed with an amethyst purple apex like the petals. It has a bright orange patch on either side of the rich maroon-purple throat and a white band in front of it.

This species grows best suspended from a block of wood or tree fern or in a teak basket in very bright light. It needs to be watered daily throughout the growing period in the summer but much less frequently during the winter. Weekly misting over will prevent the stems shrivelling too much.

Dendrobium wardianum
Warner

This is a more robust orchid than the preceding species but the flowers are rather similar. The strongest plants come from Burma, but the ones which Warner illustrated and described in his *'Select Orchidaceous Plants'* (1862) came from Assam. They have smaller but brighter flowers. It is now known throughout the Himalayan region of southeast Asia, from northeast India through Burma and Thailand to southwest China, from 1300 to 2000 m above sea level.

Stems pendent, swollen at the nodes, 30-100 cm long. Leaves bright green, deciduous. The flowers are usually borne in groups of 2-3 and are 7-10 cm in diameter. Sepals and petals waxy, white with the tips marked with amethyst purple, the petals more so than the narrower sepals. The

D. wardianum
Louis Vogelpoel

basal part of the lip is bright yellow with two maroon blotches in the throat. The front part is white with an amethyst-purple tip.

This is another species which grows well in a well drained pot or basket suspended in bright light. It needs a short dry period in the brightest possible light during the winter to induce flowering.

Dendrobium gratiosissimum
Reichb.f.
(Syn. *D. bullerianum* Bateman
D. boxallii Reichb.f.)

This species was one of the numerous discoveries of the Rev. Charles Parish in Burma in 1865, but is now also known from northeast India, Thailand, Laos and China. In cultivation the stems do not always develop the swollen nodes which are so characteristic of plants in the wild.

Stems upright or pendent, slender at the base but slightly thickened towards the apex, often thickened at the nodes, 30-50 cm long. Leaves light green, soon deciduous. Flowers in groups of 2-3 from the leafless stems, 5-6 cm across. The sepals and petals are

Opposite:
D. falconeri
Louis Vogelpoel

D. gratiosissimum
Louis Vogelpoel

white, tipped with pale rose purple, more so on the slightly broader petals. The lip is broadly ovate, white with a rose-purple tip and a deep yellow circular blotch covering most of its surface.

Less often seen in cultivation today, this species presents no difficulties to the dendrobium grower and flowers every spring after a cool, bright, dry winter.

Dendrobium pendulum Roxb.
(Syn. *D. crassinode* Benson & Reichb.f.)

This plant is easily recognised by the striking, rounded swellings just below each node and the constrictions between the swellings. Seidenfaden has likened the stems to a rosary. It was first introduced by Col. Benson from Burma although it had previously been collected from Thailand and earlier than that from northeast India (Chittagong). It is also recorded from Laos and China.

The pseudobulbs are pendent, curved, 30-60 cm long, with characteristically swollen nodes and constricted internodes. Leaves rather narrow, soon deciduous. The flowers are solitary or in groups of 2-3 from the upper nodes. The petals are much wider than the sepals and both are white, heavily tipped with mauve purple. The lip is rounded, white

D. pendulum
E.A. Schelpe

with a large deep yellow blotch over the basal half and a mauve purple apex. Some flowers lack the mauve-purple colouration.

This plant is always a talking point in a collection because of its curious stems. Plants grow best attached to a piece of tree fern fibre or in a small basket suspended in a bright position in the greenhouse and kept on the dry side during the winter.

Dendrobium findlayanum Parish & Reichb.f.

This species is recorded as a lithophyte in the higher parts of the mountain range that separates Burma from Thailand. Imported plants flowered for the first time in England in 1877. They are not often seen today, but have been exported from Thailand recently.

Stems upright or pendent, 30-60 cm long, with yellowish green, club shaped swellings above the nodes, the intervening parts of the stem very slender. Leaves arise at the base of the swollen part but are soon deciduous. Flowers produced from the upper end of the swollen parts of the stem, usually in pairs, 5-7 cm across. The flowers are pale lilac except for the lip which is ochreous yellow, fading to white at the margin, sometimes with a deep blotch in the throat. The petals are much wider than the sepals.

This species survives well in a cool greenhouse where there is plenty of air movement. It requires regular and frequent watering during the summer months and less frequent watering during the winter but should not be kept completely dry.

D. findlayanum var. maculatum 'Westfield'
E.A. Schelpe

Dendrobium parishii Reichb.f.

This rather small species has a delightful scent on sunny days, variously described as being like rhubarb or raspberries. It was first introduced by the Rev. Charles Parish from Burma to Messrs. Low and more recently it has often been imported from Thailand. It is also known in northeast India, Laos, Vietnam and southwest China.

D. parishii
H.R. Folkersma (Kew collection)

The stems are short and rather thick, often somewhat curved or apparently misshapen, up to 30 cm long but usually much shorter in cultivation, sometimes very long in the wild, upright or pendent. The light green leaves are soon deciduous. The flowers are solitary or borne in bunches of 2-3, produced simultaneously along the apical half of the leafless stems. The petals are slightly wider than the sepals and both are rosy amethyst-purple. The downy lip is ovate, the same colour as the petals but with a deep maroon blotch on each side within. There is a small white central callus and the column is also white. A pure white form is very lovely but rare.

This species is recorded in dry deciduous forest in Thailand where the plants are short with thick stems. In shady, more humid habitats, it becomes much longer and pendent. It is very amenable to cultivation in a warm and humid greenhouse, requiring a dry period with brighter light to ripen the pseudobulbs before flowering.

D. devonianum
Joyce Stewart

Dendrobium devonianum Paxton

This summer-flowering species is immediately identified by its colouration and fringed lip. It was first introduced from the Khasia hills by Gibson to the Duke of Devonshire's gardens at Chatsworth in 1837. It has since been discovered throughout a wide area of northeast India, in Bhutan, Burma, Thailand and southwest China.

The slender stems are terete and pendulous, up to 1 m long. The pale green leaves are soon deciduous. The flowers are solitary or in pairs on slender stalks along the upper part of the stems, 5 cm across. The petals are much wider than the sepals and both are white, tipped with amethyst purple, more deeply so on the petals. The lip is broadly cordate, white, with two orange yellow blotches towards the base and a purple one at the apex, strongly fringed at the margin; the segments of the fringe are branched.

The flowers of this widespread species are rather variable in colouration and several varieties have been proposed. All grow well in a cool or intermediate greenhouse where they can be given bright light during the winter and spring months.

Dendrobium primulinum Lindl.

This widespread species appears to have been introduced to cultivation in 1857. It comes from the lower slopes of the Himalayan region, between 300 and 1300 m, both from northwest and northeast India, Nepal, Burma,

Left:
D. primulinum
E.A. Schelpe

Right:
D. polyanthum
Louis Vogelpoel

Thailand, Laos, Vietnam and southwest China. The flowers are rather variable in size and the name var. *giganteum* has been proposed for some of the larger ones. The name refers to the cowslip fragrance of the flowers which open early in spring.

Stems pendent or erect, terete and thick, 30-45 cm long. Leaves varying in size, the upper ones smaller, but all soon deciduous. The flowers are solitary or in pairs, each 5-7 cm across. The sepals and petals are similar, rather narrow, pale mauve lilac. The lip is broader than long, funnel shaped, pale primrose yellow with some purplish streaks.

This plant is not difficult to grow in an intermediate or warm greenhouse if it can be moved to cooler conditions for the winter months to induce flowering.

Dendrobium polyanthum Lindl.
(Syn. *D. cretaceum* Lindl.)

A somewhat similar Indian species with white flowers. However, the petals are usually rather longer than the sepals and the rounded lip is yellow towards the base with a few reddish lines in the throat.

Dendrobium aphyllum (Roxb.) Fischer
(Syn. *D. cucullatum* R.Br.
D. pierardii Roxb. ex Hook.)

This is one of the commonest dendrobiums from the hotter regions of India, being recorded in the hot valleys of Sikkim and in many of the forested areas around the Bay of Bengal including some of the mangroves. Further afield it has also been collected from Nepal, Bhutan, Burma and all parts of southeast Asia including southwest China. Horticulturally it has always been a favourite. It was probably the first *Dendrobium* to be introduced to cultivation in

D. aphyllum
Louis Vogelpoel

England at the end of the eighteenth century and is known to have flowered in Liverpool in 1821. In appearance it is somewhat like a much more slender form of *D. primulinum* with a differently shaped lip. Seidenfaden (1985) has reviewed the problems relating to the nomenclature of this species in great detail.

Stems slender and pendulous, up to 1 m or more in length. Leaves short and narrow, soon deciduous. The flowers are usually produced in pairs, each 3-5 cm across, along the upper two thirds of each stem. When flowering simultaneously, as they usually do, they are a spectacular sight. The sepals and petals are pale rosy-mauve, semi-transparent, the petals somewhat wider than the sepals. The downy lip is broadly triangular, tubular in the basal part, pale primrose yellow with some purple streaks near the base.

Plants of this species grow well mounted on a slab of bark or tree fern fibre or established in a basket. If they are watered and fed continuously during the summer months the stems become very long, with a promise of many flowers in the following spring after a completely dry winter.

Dendrobium anosmum Lindl.
(Syn. *D. macrophyllum* Lindl.
D. macranthum Hook.
D. superbum Reichb.f.)

This superb species was first introduced from the Philippines by Hugh Cuming and flowered in the nursery of Messrs. Loddiges in 1839. It is now known to be one of the most widespread of all dendrobiums and has been recorded also from Sri Lanka, throughout the Malay Peninsula, in Thailand, Indonesia and New Guinea. Unfortunately Lindley, in 1839, overlooked the fact that the French botanist A. Richard had already used the name *Dendrobium macrophyllum* for a different species

D. anosmum
E.A. Schelpe

from New Guinea (sect. *Latouria*, see p.78) so re-described this species as *D. anosmum* in 1845. Reichenbach's apt name, *D. superbum*, was not published until 1861 and refers to the same plant.

The stems are thick and pendulous, 1-3 m long though usually shorter in cultivation. Leaves large and light green but soon deciduous. The flowers sometimes have a strong scent of rhubarb, and are borne in pairs throughout the length of the stem, each 7-10 cm across. The petals are almost twice as wide as the sepals and a rich magenta purple. The lip is cordate, a rich deep purple, darker towards the base. It is downy over its whole surface and has a minutely fringed margin.

Very large plants of this species can be established if sufficient space is available. It grows well in a basket of well drained compost and needs an ample supply of water and weak fertiliser during the summer months, followed by a dry period when the plants are leafless.

Dendrobium tortile Lindl.

Another species that is widespread at rather low altitudes in the Himalayan region, this *Dendrobium* was first introduced by the firm of Veitch through the efforts of Thomas Lobb who sent it from Tenasserim. It is obviously close to *D. primulinum* and *D. aphyllum* but is easily distinguished from these two species by the twisted sepals and petals to which the name refers.

The pseudobulbous stems are rather short and club-shaped, narrow below, up to 20-30 cm long, becoming furrowed when old. The narrow leaves are light green and soon deciduous. The flowers are solitary or borne in short inflorescences of 2-3, each c. 7 cm across. The sepals and petals are pale rosy lilac, sometimes very pale, both are twisted, the petals more so. The lip is round, pale primrose yellow with a few purple streaks and a small purplish blotch at the apex.

This species flowers in late spring or early summer on leafless canes that are a year or more old.

D. tortile
Jean Dryden

Dendrobium signatum Reichb.f.
(Syn. *D. hildebrandii* Rolfe)

Is a rather similar species but the plants are usually stouter, rather like those of *D. nobile*. Some botanists consider that it is only a variety of *D. tortile*. The twisted sepals and petals are always white or cream and there may or may not be two purplish blotches, one on each side, towards the base of the lip.

D. signatum
Louis Vogelpoel

Dendrobium crystallinum Reichb.f.

First discovered in Burma, this species was introduced to cultivation by Messrs. Veitch at their Chelsea nursery in 1868. It is easily recognised among all the similar species of *Dendrobium* by the conical anther cap which bears numerous crystalline papillae at its apex. The species is now known to have a wide distribution from Burma eastwards through Thailand, Laos, Cambodia and Vietnam from 400 to 1700 m above sea level.

The pseudobulbous stems are tufted, upright or pendulous, 30-45 cm long. The leaves are linear, pale green, and soon deciduous. The flowers are solitary or in short inflorescences of 2-3, each c. 5 cm across, sheathed in a long membranous bract that covers half the peduncle. The sepals and petals are white, usually with a pale ameythst blotch towards the tip, the petals wider than the sepals. The lip is rounded, deep yellow bordered with white, and usually with an amethyst coloured apex like the petals.

This is one of the more slender species in this section, but it is just as easy to grow and flower as the others if careful attention is paid to the necessary seasonal changes in water supply.

Dendrobium crepidatum Lindl. & Paxt.

First introduced from Assam, this species flowered in 1850 at Westonbirt in the collection of R.S. Holford. It is now known throughout the Himalayan region, including Nepal, Sikkim and Bhutan, and into Burma, Thailand, Laos, Vietnam and southwest China. The plants in India often have smaller flowers that do not open fully and are usually self-pollinating.

The pseudobulbous stems are rather thick, pendent at maturity, 30-45 cm long. The leaves are thin and soon deciduous. The flowers are borne on pale purple pedicels in groups of 2-3, each 3-4 cm across. The sepals and petals are rather waxy, white but slightly tinted with lilac. The lip is deep yellow with a white border, and

D. crystallinum
Louis Vogelpoel

D. crepidatum
Louis Vogelpoel

there is a fold on each side near the base forming a slipper-like cavity. *'Crepidatum'* means 'wearing slippers'.

This species flowers in the early summer as the new growths are beginning to grow. Watering must be performed carefully so that growth is not inhibited and the flowers not spoiled.

Dendrobium lituiflorum Lindl.

This rather delicate species is close to *D. nobile* but is easily recognised by the cornet shaped lip (*'lituus'* means 'a sort of trumpet'). Several different colour varieties have been described, including white forms, but the best ones are a rich purple. It has been recorded from northeast India, Burma, Thailand, Laos and southwest China.

The slender stems are often pendulous, 40-60 cm long. The leaves are small and soon deciduous. The flowers arise in groups of 2-3, each 5-6 cm across. The sepals and petals are at best a rich amethyst purple, the petals usually darker and wider. The lip is like the mouth of a trumpet, rich maroon purple within, surrounded by a pale or white zone and with a purple margin.

This species is easily maintained on a chunk of tree fern fibre or in a small basket of well-drained compost. It usually flowers in April or May, after a dry winter and as the new growths begin to form.

D. amoenum
E.A. Schelpe

Dendrobium amoenum Lindl.

Pressed specimens of this species became known to science more than 40 years before this plant was introduced to cultivation in 1874. It was first collected in Nepal, and later in other parts of the Indian Himalaya and in Burma. It occurs in areas where the climate is temperate throughout the year and there is frost on the ground in winter. The medium sized flowers are scented of violets, particularly when the plant is in the sunlight.

The pseudobulbous stems are slender, usually pendent, 30-50 cm long. The leaves are light green and soon deciduous. The flowers are usually solitary, sometimes in inflorescences of 2-3, each c. 5 cm across. The sepals and petals are broad, white, tipped with amethyst purple. The lip is broadly ovate, minutely notched, amethyst purple bordered with white and with a yellow blotch near the base.

This species flowers during the summer months after a prolonged dry and cool period.

D. lituiflorum
E.A. Schelpe

Dendrobium transparens Wall. ex Lindl.

This is another species that was first introduced to botanists by

D. transparens
Louis Vogelpoel

Dr. Wallich in the early part of the last century and then reintroduced as a living plant much later. Thomas Lobb sent it to the firm of Veitch in 1852. It grows in the Indian part of the Himalayan region and also in Burma and usually flowers in March.

The stems are slender and usually pendulous, 30-50 cm long. The leaves are light green and deciduous. The flowers are borne on purplish pedicels, in short racemes of 2-3 on the leafless stems, each 3-4 cm across. The petals are wider than the sepals, both white and tinted with pale rosy-mauve towards the tips. The lip is ovate-oblong, enclosing the column at its base, white with two deep purple blotches on the surface and pale mauve purple at the front margin.

This beautiful species was formerly abundant in the warmer valleys of the lower slopes of the Himalaya. The flowers are borne at the end of the dry winter season, before the new growths appear.

Dendrobium loddigesii Rolfe

This dwarf plant has an unusual habit of growth as the pseudobulbs branch freely, new ones arising about half way along the length of the preceding one. It spreads like a mat over the surface of branches and rocks and forms a large mass of stems. Its origin was for a long time rather confused but it is now known from southern China and Laos.

The stems are slender and only 7-10 cm long, somewhat thickened in the upper part. The leaves are small, light green and soon deciduous. The flowers are solitary, each borne on a slender pedicel about as long as the leaves and 3-4 cm across. The sepals and petals are rosy lilac, the latter much wider. The broad lip is flat except at the base, deep orange yellow with a pale lilac border.

This plant grows easily over a piece of tree fern fibre or bark and needs to be kept cool and dry in winter. It is very spectacular when covered with flowers in spring. However the young growths are very tempting to slugs, and careful reconnaissance is necessary when the plants are developing early in the summer.

D. loddigesii
P.J. Cribb

Group 2. Inflorescences with 1-3 flowers at each of several nodes; sepals and petals yellow or white without pink or purple tips.

Dendrobium senile Parish & Reichb.f.

This remarkable species differs from all others by its dwarf size and covering of long white hairs. The latter feature apparently suggested the specific name — *'senilis'* means 'resembling old age'. It was originally sent to England for cultivation by the Rev. Charles Parish from Burma, but has also been recorded since then at medium and high altitudes in Thailand and Laos.

The pseudobulbous stems are short and squat, 3-8 cm long, rarely longer, covered with long white hairs. The leaves are borne at the nodes towards the apex and are light green and similarly hairy but soon deciduous. The flowers are borne from the apical nodes, singly or in pairs, each about 4 cm across, pale golden yellow, the lip slightly darker than the rest of the flower, sometimes greenish.

This unusual species is not easy in cultivation but appears to thrive if mounted on a piece of wood and hung up where the air movement is fierce for much of the year. When new growths appear it needs to be watered and fed generously for a few months, then treated to a long dry season before it flowers in the late winter.

Dendrobium capillipes Reichb.f.

This is also a dwarf species which came originally from Burma but it is not hairy. It is the smallest among the yellow flowered species of *Dendrobium* and the flowers are almost larger than the plants. It is now known from highland regions of Thailand, Laos, Vietnam and southwest China as well as northeast India.

The dwarf stems grow in tufts

D. senile
G. Nicholson (Kew collection)

and are rarely more than 5-8 cm tall. Only 1-2 leaves are borne on each stem, with whitish sheaths, and they are soon deciduous. The flowers are borne in slender inflorescences, either solitary or up to 5 on each peduncle, and are a rich golden yellow with an orange blotch on the lip, each 3-4 cm across. The sepals are narrow and short, the petals larger and broad, and the lip is large and round.

This neat species grows well in a pot or basket of well drained compost. It needs to be watered sparingly during the winter and hung in a brightly lit space to promote flowering early in the spring.

D. capillipes
Joyce Stewart

Dendrobium dixanthum Reichb.f.

The specific name of this plant refers to the two shades of yellow in the flowers which are quite prolific towards the apex of the slender pseudobulbs. It has been known in cultivation since the middle of the last century, after being introduced by the Rev. Charles Parish from Burma through Messrs. Low. It is also now known from northern Thailand.

Stems long and slender, upright or pendent, 60-90 cm long. Leaves narrow and bright green, soon deciduous. The flowers are produced in racemes of 2-5 from the leafless stems, each c. 3 cm across. The sepals are narrow and pointed, the petals wider and rounded. The lip is large and conspicuous, finely fringed at the margin and retuse at the apex.

This species is usually pendent in greenhouses and grows well in a small pot or basket of well drained compost. A bright, cooler, dry period in winter promotes flowering in spring and plenty of water and fertiliser should be given during the summer months when growth of new stems is continuous.

D. dixanthum
Louis Vogelpoel

D. heterocarpum
Louis Vogelpoel

Dendrobium heterocarpum Lindl.
(Syn. *D. aureum* Lindl.
D. rhombeum Lindl.)

This is the most widely distributed species in the section and probably the most widely distributed of all dendrobiums. It is recorded from Sri Lanka, throughout the Himalayan region from the northwest of India to southwest China, and southwards through Malaysia, Sumatra and Java to the Philippines. Throughout this wide area there is considerable variation in its size but there is usually little difficulty in naming the plants in flower because of the rather narrow lip. Lindley, however, thought the species should be split into several entities and some botanists still support this view.

Stems erect, rather stout, 20-50 cm high, becoming yellowish as they age. The leaves are light green and soon deciduous. The flowers are produced in groups of 2-3 from the upper nodes of well ripened stems, each 4-7 cm across. The sepals and petals are cream or pale yellow, rather similar, the petals only slightly wider than the sepals. The lip is buff yellow streaked with red or orange, narrowly triangular in shape but often strongly curled, with a narrow spur at its base.

This species is still widely grown and always pleasing because of its primrose fragrance. It has been the ancestor of a wide range of hybrids of the *'nobile*-type'.

Dendrobium chrysanthum Lindl.

This species is easily recognised by producing its flowers on the current year's growth, usually before the leaves have fallen, in the autumn months. It was first introduced by Dr. Nathaniel Wallich who brought plants to England from the Calcutta Botanic Garden in 1828. It is now known to be widely distributed in the warmer parts of northeast India, Bhutan, Burma, Tibet, Thailand, Laos, Vietnam and southwest China.

The long slender stems may reach 3 m in length and are

D. chrysanthum
Jean Dryden

D. ochreatum
Louis Vogelpoel

clothed in leaves throughout. The flowers may be solitary or in racemes of 2-6, sometimes hidden below the leaves but usually enhanced by their contrasting colour. They are bright orange yellow with two reddish brown blotches in the base of the lip. The petals are slightly wider than the sepals. The rounded lip has a finely fringed margin and is hairy on both surfaces.

This species is an exception to the rule of keeping dendrobiums dry in winter. It seems to grow throughout the year and, while it needs plenty of light and air movement, the compost should not be allowed to dry out if maximum growth is to be achieved. It does best established in a wooden basket in a warm house, and the new growths emerge soon after flowering.

Dendrobium ochreatum Lindl. (Syn. *D. cambridgeanum* Paxt.) seems to be rather similar and has sometimes been confused with *D. chrysanthum*. It usually has shorter pseudobulbs and the sepals and petals are pointed at the apex, not rounded. The rich golden yellow lip has a deep maroon purple blotch near the base, a shorter fringe at the apex, and on the lower surface it is hairy only along the border. This species is unusual among dendrobiums in growing its new growths during the winter months and flowering on them while the leaves are still present in spring. It therefore needs to be kept in a warm house during the winter and moved to much cooler conditions and kept dry during the summer.

D. chrysocrepis
E.A. Schelpe

Dendrobium chrysocrepis Parish & Reichb.f.

This is often described as a curious species because of its slipper shaped lip. In fact it is somewhat similar to that of *D. moschatum* (see below p.45), though smaller and bright golden yellow. It was first collected in Burma by the Rev. Charles Parish and sent to Kew where it flowered in 1872. It is also known from northeast India.

Stems slender and short, usually upright, thickened in the upper part from a slender base, and often flattened. Leaves light green and deciduous. The flowers are golden yellow, 2-3 cm across, usually solitary from the old leafless stems. The sepals and petals are similar, short and wide, the lip somewhat pear shaped with a rounded incurved margin, velvety.

This species grows without difficulty as a mounted specimen in a cool greenhouse. It is kept on the dry side during the cooler winter months. It frequently produces 'keikis' from the upper nodes of the stem instead of flowering.

D. albosanguineum
Louis Vogelpoel

Dendrobium albosanguineum Lindl.

This seems to be rather a rare species but has several times been introduced from Burma and Thailand. It is a robust plant with easily recognised, large flowers that are milk white with blood red markings on the lip.

Stems erect, rather stout, 15-30 cm high. Leaves light green, deciduous. The inflorescences are produced near the apex of the stems, 2-3-flowered, the flowers each nearly 8 cm across. The flowers are white or pale creamy yellow, the petals wider than the sepals. The lip is broadly obovate and the reddish purple markings are raised above its surface like a birthmark.

The striking flowers of this species are produced from one and two year old stems early in the summer. Plants need good light especially in the winter and spring, and grow best mounted or in a basket so that they can dry out rapidly after watering.

Dendrobium bensoniae Reichb.f.

This is widely regarded as one of the finest of the white flowered dendrobiums in this section. It is recorded from India and Burma and was first introduced by a Col. Benson in Burma and named after his wife. In many ways it is rather similar to *D. nobile* but completely lacks the pinkish colouration of that species.

The stems are robust, erect, 20-80 cm tall. The leaves are light green and deciduous. The flowers are borne in groups of 2-3 from the upper nodes, each c. 8 cm across, creamy white with an orange yellow centre to the rounded lip and two maroon dots in its throat which are sometimes confluent. Some plants are known in which the dark markings are absent.

This species responds well to the usual treatment for the *nobile*-type dendrobiums, with a warm wet growing season and a cooler dry season during the winter months.

D. bensoniae
Louis Vogelpoel

Dendrobium friedericksianum Reichb.f.

This species is endemic in Thailand where it is greatly valued for its ease of flowering and long-lasting qualities. It occurs in the warm forests at low elevation in the southeast of Thailand.

The stems are robust above a very narrow base, erect or almost so, up to 45 cm long. The leaves are soon deciduous. The flowers are borne in small inflorescences of 3-4 during the cooler months, each one 5-6 cm across. The sepals and petals are waxy, chrome yellow. The lip is a slightly darker yellow and may or may not have two maroon blotches in the throat.

This species grows easily in a warm greenhouse but needs to be kept on the dry side during the cooler months.

D. friedericksianum
Louis Vogelpoel

Group 3 Inflorescences with 1-3 flowers at each of several nodes; sepals and petals orange red

Dendrobium unicum Seid.

This species has only been introduced to cultivation quite recently but is very distinctive and desirable on account of its orange red flowers. It is known from Thailand and Laos.

Pseudobulbs slender, upright or pendulous, up to 25 cm long but often shorter, becoming brown or blackish with age. The leaves light green, soon deciduous. The inflorescences are borne on the upper nodes and carry 2-4 bright orange flowers. The sepals and petals are narrow and strongly reflexed, the lip dull pale brownish orange with darker lines and a 3-ridged callus along the centre.

Small colourful plants of this species are a welcome addition to a collection and flower in early summer. However, the plants scarcely seem to stop growing and need a certain amount of moisture throughout the year.

D. unicum
Louis Vogelpoel

Group 4 Inflorescences long and pendulous with 5-15 flowers from the upper nodes; flowers yellow or pinkish yellow

Dendrobium pulchellum Roxb. ex Lindl.
(Syn. *D. dalhousieanum* Paxt.)

This is the largest of the orchids in this section. The robust pseudobulbs frequently bear their first flowers in the first year of growth, amongst the leaves, and do so again for several years in succession even after they become leafless. They can be recognised even when leafless by the purplish markings on the young internodes. This species is widespread in the Himalayan region, from Nepal eastwards through India, Burma, Thailand, Laos, Vietnam and Malaya. It has been in cultivation for many years, starting at Chatsworth in 1837 where it was introduced from the Calcutta Botanic Garden.

The stems are usually erect, robust, at least 1 m long and often 2 m. The leaves are borne towards the apex of the stems and last for several seasons. The inflorescences are lateral from near the apex of the stems, 15-20 cm long and bearing 5-12 flowers each 5-10 cm across. The sepals and petals are usually pale yellow tipped with rose. The ovate lip is boat shaped, pinkish or yellowish, covered with soft velvety hairs, and with two deep reddish-maroon blotches in the base.

D. pulchellum
Jean Dryden

This plant is a great joy when it flowers well. In a suitably warm and humid greenhouse there seems to be no problem provided a slightly cooler and less humid season follows the period of maximum growth.

Dendrobium moschatum (Buch.-Ham.) Sw.
(Syn. *D. calceolaria* Carey ex Hook.
D. cupreum Herbert)

This species is also robust and somewhat similar in growth habit to the preceding but the stems lack any kind of markings. The apricot or pale copper coloured flowers are most attractive but unfortunately usually last for less than a week. This species is widespread throughout the

D. moschatum
Louis Vogelpoel

warmer parts of the Himalayan region, from northwest India to Laos and recorded from all countries in between.

The pseudobulbous stems are cylindrical, erect, 120-200 cm tall, leafy throughout. The leaves are medium to dark green and usually persist for two years. The inflorescences come from the upper nodes of two year old stems and bear 7-15 flowers, each 8-10 cm in diameter. The sepals and petals are pinkish yellow tipped with rose, the petals wider and rounded. The lip is slipper shaped, incurved at the margin, covered with a velvety pile on both surfaces, orange within and bearing 5 rows of longer hairs and two deep maroon blotches at the base.

This species used to be commonly seen in collections but its large size and the short lasting flowers have made it less popular today. It is not difficult to grow in a pot or basket of well drained compost.

D. fimbriatum var. oculatum
E.A. Schelpe

Dendrobium fimbriatum Hook.

This is another large and robust species but the pseudobulbs are usually pendulous. It was first seen in England in the Liverpool Botanic Garden, to which it had been sent by Nathaniel Wallich from Nepal, in 1822. Fifteen years later the var. *oculatum*, distinguished by the maroon blotch in the base of the lip, was sent to Chatsworth from the Khasia Hills. Today the spotted form is much more frequently seen in collections than the golden form but both are very floriferous.

The narrow stems are 1.2-2 m long, upright or pendulous. Dark green leaves are borne along the upper half in two ranks. The inflorescences arise along the upper part of the stems, usually after the leaves have fallen, and bear 7-12 flowers each 5-8 cm across. The sepals and petals are rounded, clear golden yellow, the petals usually wider than the sepals. The lip is rounded or quadrate with a fringed margin, brighter yellow within and sometimes with a dark maroon blotch at the base.

The plants without spots in the flowers are usually smaller but equally attractive. The spotted form is widespread throughout the Himalayan region but the unspotted form appears to be less common. Both are welcome if there is space to maintain them because they are so floriferous; hundreds of flowers are not uncommon on a well grown plant.

D. gibsonii
E.A. Schelpe

Dendrobium gibsonii Lindl.
(Syn. *D. fuscatum* Lindl.)

Also very widespread and has been considered by some botanists as a variety of *D. fimbriatum*. However, the plants are consistently smaller, as are the flowers. The apex of the lip is quite different in its type of hairiness and there are usually two small maroon spots in the throat, one on each side. This species was first collected by J.D. Hooker in the hot valleys of the Sikkim Himalaya and later by the Duke of Devonshire's collector, Gibson, in the Khasia Hills.

Dendrobium chryseum Rolfe
(Syn. *D. clavatum* Lindl.
D. aurantiacum Reichb.f.
D. flaviflorum Hayata
D. denneanum Kerr)

This species is easily recognised by its branching inflorescence and the conspicuous bracts along the peduncles and at the base of each pedicel. It is widespread throughout the Himalayan region and has been in cultivation a long time under a variety of names. Its tangled nomenclature has been reviewed by Seidenfaden (1985).

The stems are tufted, upright although rather slender, 30-60 cm high. The leaves appear from the upper nodes of the stems. The inflorescences are simple or branching with conspicuous straw coloured bracts and 4-15 golden yellow flowers each 2-3 cm across. The petals are wider than the sepals; the fringed lip is orbicular, hairy, and with or without a dark coloured blotch at its base.

This species grows easily under similar conditions to *D. gibsonii*, and like it is of more manageable size in a small greenhouse than some of the others in this group.

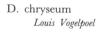

D. chryseum
Louis Vogelpoel

Chapter 5
Section Callista

Most of the orchids in this section of *Dendrobium* are found in cultivation and are easily recognised by their attractive inflorescences, pendent like bunches of golden grapes from the dark green upright stems. Many of the species take a much longer period of 'rest' than other dendrobiums, but once they have started into growth, usually in early summer, their development is rapid.

The pseudobulbous stems grow close together from a basal rhizome. Each stem is made up of several nodes and is rather narrow at the base, swollen and sometimes angular above, and bearing 1-5 leaves close together near the apex. Each dark green, rather leathery leaf appears to be directly inserted on the stem, with a very short sheathing base.

The flowers are borne in pendent racemes from among the leaves, usually many and either white or yellow, rarely pale pink, with darker yellow on the lip. The sepals are usually rather similar in size and shape, but the petals are wider, sometimes with minutely ragged edges. The lip is rather wide or orbicular, lacking side lobes, and rather hairy or papillose on the inner surface. Near the base of the lip is a transverse callus and there is a concave nectary at the foot of the column.

This section is confined to continental Asia with a distribution range extending from the Himalaya eastwards through the mountainous areas of Burma, Thailand, Laos and Vietnam to southwestern China and southwards to the northern part of Malaysia.

Dendrobium lindleyi Steud.
(Syn. *D. aggregatum* Roxb.)

This species was discovered in northern India and flowered first in cultivation in Calcutta, then at the Royal Horticultural Society's garden in London in 1834. Its distribution is now known to extend from Sikkim, Assam and Bengal through Burma, into Thailand, and also through Laos and Vietnam to Yunnan and Hainan in southwest China. The name *D. lindleyi* has to be used for this species since Roxburgh's *D. aggregatum* by which it has long been known was published later than *D. aggregatum* H.B. & K., which is a *Maxillaria* species.

The pseudobulbs are somewhat tapered at both ends and strongly ribbed. They usually lie flat against the substratum, or only slightly raised above it, and are rather short, 5-10 cm long. Each bears a single, greyish green leaf at its apex. The inflorescence arises laterally from one or more of the upper nodes and carries many golden flowers which darken with age. The lip sometimes has several darker orange bands in the throat and is hairy only towards the base.

D. lindleyi
Louis Vogelpoel

This species is recorded from altitudes of 500 to 2000 m. It grows as an epiphyte on the trunks and branches of deciduous trees and is consequently fully exposed to the sun during the winter before flowering in the spring. It needs bright light in a cool but humid greenhouse and grows best attached to a slab of wood or cork oak bark. Several months of drought during the winter months are essential to promote flowering.

Dendrobium jenkinsii Wall. ex Lindl.
(Syn. *D. aggregatum* Roxb. var. *jenkinsii* (Wall. ex Lindl.) King and Pantling)

This dwarf species was discovered in 1836 by a military officer named Jenkins in Assam. It was sent to England for cultivation through the Calcutta Botanic Garden. It is reported as growing in mixed populations with *D. lindleyi* but is always easily distinguished from that species by its differently shaped pseudobulbs and few flowered inflorescence. In cultivation together they are also quite distinct.

The mature pseudobulbs are only 2-3 cm long and laterally compressed. They form a mat which appears to creep over the bark of trees, sometimes becoming upright and forming dense tufts. Each pseudobulb bears a single apical leaf and a 1-3-flowered inflorescence. The flowers are large and pure gold in colour. The lip is almost heart shaped with a retuse apex.

Although less common in cultivation than *D. lindleyi*, plants of this species are often imported with it and misidentified. It needs similar conditions of light and humidity to grow and flower well.

D. jenkinsii
E.A. Schelpe

Dendrobium chrysotoxum Lindl.
(Syn. *D. suavissimum* Reichb.f.
D. chrysotoxum Lindl. var. *suavissimum* (Reichb.f.) Veitch)

The 'Golden Arch Dendrobium' was apparently imported to England from Burma as a living plant in 1858. The var. *suavissimum*, which has a pair of brownish purple blotches at the base of the lip, was sent to Hugh Low in 1874. Some authors consider that the two varieties should be regarded as distinct species, but there are a number of species of *Dendrobium* which exhibit two colour forms, depending on the presence or absence of blotches on the lip, so they are included together here. Both forms have a wide distribution range from the Himalaya through southeast Asia to Yunnan, usually occurring above 2000 m.

The pseudobulbs are upright, up to 30 cm long, and very much swollen in the upper half, tapering again towards the apex. They become grooved or angular and a deep yellow colour when old. Two to five dark green leaves are borne at the apex. The inflorescence is a multi-flowered arching raceme. The flowers are well spaced, deep yellow, and up to 5 cm wide. The lip is a slightly darker yellow, with or without one large or two smaller deep maroon patches towards the base and a finely fringed and crisped margin.

These plants require as much sun as possible in cultivation to encourage flowering. They seem to be more tolerant of moisture at

D. chrysotoxum
E.A. Schelpe

the roots than some of the other species in this section and the pseudobulbs retain their shape better if water is withheld from the plants for only a short period during the winter.

Dendrobium harveyanum Reichb.f.

This striking species was placed in this section by growers when it was first introduced but more recently it has often been included in section *Dendrobium*. The growth habit is just like a slender form of *D. chrysotoxum* or *D. farmeri* and the inflorescences, though few-flowered, arise in the same way. It was first introduced from Burma and has also been recorded from Vietnam and Thailand but seems to be always rare.

Stems fusiform, slender at the base and above, 15-20 cm long. The leaves are clustered together near the apex of the stem, dark green and persistent. The inflorescences arise from the upper nodes, bearing 3-7 flowers, each c. 5 cm across. The flowers are bright canary yellow with narrow and acute sepals, wider petals that have a remarkable, branched fringe around the margin, and an orbicular, papillose lip that also has a fringed margin but less pronounced.

This species grows well adjacent to *D. farmeri* and under similar conditions.

D. harveyanum
E.A. Schelpe

Dendrobium brymerianum Reichb.f.

A somewhat similar and equally rarely seen species from the same area. The pseudobulbs are rather more swollen in the middle and very slender at the base. In this species, the flowers are larger but a similar shade of yellow and it is the lip which has a remarkable, fringed border.

D. brymerianum
E.A. Schelpe

D. brymerianum var. histrionicum *E.A. Schelpe*

Dendrobium brymerianum var **histrionicum** Reichb.f.

A smaller plant and the flowers have a shorter fringe except in the centre of the lip apex where it forms a prominent 'beard'.

Dendrobium densiflorum Lindl.

This golden species is a great favourite with orchid growers as it seems very easy to grow and never fails to flower after a dry, bright winter. It was first discovered in Nepal and introduced to cultivation through the Royal Horticultural Society in London. The first record of its flowering in England is in the nursery of Messrs. Loddiges in 1830. In the wild this species is recorded from altitudes above 1000 m in Nepal, through Assam and Burma, perhaps into northern Thailand and southwest China, but some authors have not distinguished it from *D. thyrsiflorum* so some of the records are doubtful. Seidenfaden considers this to be a true Himalayan species.

Stems robust and upright, 25-40 cm high, tapering towards the base and 4-6-angled above. Three to four dark green leaves are borne near the apex of each stem. The inflorescences first appear as swollen knobs below the leaves and develop rapidly to form long racemes closely set with many golden flowers. The flowers open to about 5 cm, are golden yellow with a deeper orange lip that is hairy over the whole surface.

This species is easy to maintain in a pot or basket of well-drained compost and large plants can be produced which are very spectacular when covered with flowers. Many pseudobulbs will flower over several successive seasons in good conditions, both from leafy and leafless stems.

D. densiflorum *E.A. Schelpe*

Dendrobium farmeri Paxton (Syn. *D. densiflorum* Lindl. var. *alboluteum* Hook.f.)

This species was first imported into England in 1847 by an amateur orchid grower after whom it was named. With its delicate pink and golden flowers it is one of the most beautiful in the section but unfortunately the flowers last only a few days. In the wild this species is widespread from the Khasia Hills in India southwards through Burma and Malaysia to Thailand, Laos and Vietnam.

The pseudobulbs are upright or may became pendent with age, up to 30 cm long, thickened and 4-angled in the upper part. Four or five dark green, shiny leaves are borne near the apex of each stem. The drooping inflorescence may be up to 20 cm long and carries numerous white, pale pink or lilac flowers, each 5 cm wide and well spaced. The lip is deep golden and hairy within.

D. farmeri
E.A. Schelpe

This very desirable species prefers slightly more shady conditions in cultivation than the other species in this section. High humidity is essential and plenty of water should be given when the plants are in active growth. A prolonged dry period is essential to promote flowering.

D. griffithianum Lindl.

A somewhat similar golden yellow flowered species which grows at higher elevations. Its slightly darker lip is hairy over the whole of its surface.

D. griffithianum
Louis Vogelpoel

D. thyrsiflorum
E.A. Schelpe

Dendrobium thyrsiflorum
Reichb.f. ex Andre

Although originally introduced to cultivation much later than *D. densiflorum* this species is now more widely grown than that species and massive plants with many inflorescences are sometimes seen at orchid shows. Unfortunately, like the other plants in this section, the beautiful flowers only last for about a week in perfection. In the wild it is recorded from northeast India, Burma, northern Thailand, Laos, Vietnam and China, on deciduous trees above 1200 m.

The pseudobulbs are upright and grow close together, sometimes slender and up to 45 cm long, narrowing towards the apex and grooved below. Several dark green leaves are borne near the apex. The inflorescences are large and pendulous carrying many flowers up to 5 cm wide. The sepals and petals are white, rarely flushed pink, and the lip golden yellow.

This species is as easy to maintain in cultivation as *D. densiflorum* and sometimes seems to be easier to bring into flower. Some authors consider it to be merely a white flowered form of *D. densiflorum* but we can see no reason to unite these two well known species.

Chapter 6
Section Formosae

(formerly known as *Nigrohirsutae* and *Oxygenianthe*)

The 'nigrohirsute' dendrobiums, as the name suggests, are characterised by the short black or dark brown hairs which spring from the leaf sheaths when the stems are young and sometimes throughout the life of each pseudobulb.

The stems grow upright, in tufts, and are thickened all along their length from a slightly more swollen base. They are a dull green colour, covered with the hairy sheaths of the leaves which are borne along the stems. The leaves are dull or bright green, often shiny, and last for several seasons on the plant. The inflorescences arise among the leaves, usually from the apex of the pseudobulb first, and gradually appearing at lower nodes in ensuing seasons.

The large flowers are usually borne in small groups of 1-3; they are mostly white, waxy or rather papery. Despite their somewhat fragile appearance they are very long lasting, both on and off the plant. The sepals are usually narrower than the broad petals. The lip is three lobed with the side lobes upright on either side of the column and a conspicuous mentum at its base which sometimes extends into a spur. The lip surface is not usually hairy but has conspicuous yellow or red markings on the surface of the mid-lobe.

This large section of 30-35 species has three centres of distribution in the tropical parts of Asia, northern India through Burma and Thailand to southern China, the Philippines, and 13 species are recorded in Borneo.

Dendrobium formosum
Roxb. ex Lindl.
(Syn. *D. infundibulum* Reichb.f. not Lindl.)

The type species of this section occurs from northern India throughout the Himalayan region into Thailand and Vietnam at rather lower elevations than the somewhat similar *D. infundibulum*. It has larger flowers with a shorter spur and requires warmer conditions to grow well. Specimens of *D. formosum* were introduced into cultivation much

D. formosum
E.A. Schelpe

earlier, by Dr. Roxburgh, who first discovered the species in Nepal.

The pseudobulbs are quite stout, growing close together in tufts, densely covered with short black hairs and up to 45 cm tall. Two rows of dark green leaves grow from the upper two thirds of each stem. The flowers are large, white, the petals almost round with wavy edges and 4 cm long. The lip is c. 7 cm long and yellow in the throat with a broad raised ridge along its centre. It has a short mentum at the base.

In a pot or basket this species grows well and flowers regularly in a temperate greenhouse. It needs water throughout the year and regular feeding after the new growths appear in early summer. The flowers appear along the stems in groups of 2-3 in the late winter and early spring.

D. infundibulum
E.A. Schelpe

Dendrobium infundibulum Lindl.
(Syn. *D. jamesianum* Reichb.f.)

This species has rather smaller flowers than *D. formosum* and is found at higher altitudes throughout the same region. It is said to be quite common in Thailand where suitable forest habitats still exist. The species was first introduced to cultivation by the Rev. Parish who sent it from Burma to the orchid nursery of Messrs. Low at Clapton in the 1860's. John Lindley had already named and described it from pressed specimens a few years earlier.

D. infundibulum
E.A. Schelpe

The pseudobulbs are slender, densely covered with black hairs, 30-100 cm tall. Two rows of dark green leaves are borne on the upper part of the stems and last for several years. The inflorescences carry 2-3 flowers and appear among the leaves, first at the apex of the stem and lower down on subsequent flowerings. The white flowers are up to 8 cm in diameter. The lip is 3-lobed, bears a short ridge terminating in 5 crests along its centre, and has orange or red lines in the base of the throat and in the mentum. The mentum is longer than that of *D. formosum*.

This species flowers in spring and early summer after a cooler winter and needs water throughout the year.

D. cruentum
Louis Vogelpoel

Dendrobium cruentum Reichb.f.

This easily recognised species is probably endemic in Thailand although there is an early record of its occurrence in Burma. Plants can be found on small trees in the open forests at rather low elevations throughout the country. It was first introduced to cultivation by Sander in 1884. The specific name means blood red and refers to the colour of the lip callus.

The slender pseudobulbs are swollen at the base, erect, reaching a height of c. 30 cm. They bear two rows of leaves in the upper half. The flowers are solitary or in pairs among the upper leaves and up to 5 cm in diameter. The petals are narrower than the sepals and all are pale green or yellowish cream in colour. The large, 3-lobed lip has narrow, erect, reddish side lobes and a wide midlobe that is white with a red margin and has a large warty red crest in the centre.

Although the flowers are smaller than some of the other members of this section, their attractive colouration makes this species very welcome in a collection. It is not difficult to maintain in a well-drained compost and seems to flower more or less continuously throughout the year. Individual flowers last for at least a month.

Dendrobium draconis Reichb.f.
(Syn. *D. eburneum* Reichb.f. ex Bateman)

This is another of the discoveries made by the Rev. Parish in Burma and sent to Messrs. Low in 1862. It is widely distributed in southeast Asia, and is now known from Thailand, Laos, Cambodia and Vietnam as well as Burma. It is one of the commonest dendrobiums in Thailand at altitudes between 200 and 1300 m and is immediately recognisable by the bright red throat and long narrow spur of the lip.

The pseudobulbs are rather short and robust, covered with fine black hairs and reach 20-45 cm high. The leaves are in two rows and have brown hairs on both surfaces. The inflorescences arise at the nodes and bear 2-5 flowers. The sepals are narrower than the petals, all creamy white. The lip is long with triangular side lobes; the long midlobe has a

D. draconis, wide lip form
E.A. Schelpe

D. draconis, narrow lip form
Louis Vogelpoel

wavy margin, red lines towards the base and a crest of 5 broken ridges on its surface. The slender mentum forms a spur about 2.5 cm long.

This species is easily grown in cultivation in a pot or basket of well-drained compost and thrives if kept at intermediate temperatures with high humidity and good air movement. It is usually spring-flowering and the flowers last for about 3 weeks.

Dendrobium cariniferum
Reichb.f.

This species is easily recognised by the sepals which are prominently keeled along the midline on the outer surface — 'bearing keels' is the meaning of the specific name. It was first seen in flower in England in 1869, having been imported from Burma, and sent to Reichenbach for naming. It is now known from northeast India, Burma, Thailand, Laos, Cambodia, Vietnam and southern China where it grows in light shade between 700 and 1000 m altitude.

Pseudobulbs cylindric and robust, 15-25 cm long, clothed with brownish-black hairs. The leaves are in two rows but soon deciduous. The flowers are solitary or in 2-3 flowered inflorescences near the apex of the stems, 2-3 cm across. The sepals and petals are white to pale fawn, fading to white with yellowish tips, the sepals keeled on the back. The lip is 3-lobed and mostly bright orange with hairs along the

D. cariniferum
Jean Dryden

veins, and a long brownish spur at the base. The ovary is distinctly 3-winged.

This species is very similar to *D. draconis* in its growth and flowering habit.

Dendrobium williamsonii Day & Reichb.f.

A very similar species and the two have often been confused, especially in herbaria. There are several differences in the flowers which are not difficult to see in living specimens. *D. williamsonii* lacks the keels on the sepals and ovary. It also has a broader lip, which has only a small band of bright red colouration across its surface and has much longer hairs especially towards the front. Some botanists consider that these two species are not distinct, in which case *D. williamsonii* is the earlier name.

Dendrobium longicornu Lindl.

This species occurs at lower altitudes in the Himalayan region, throughout India from Nepal eastwards, and is also recorded from Burma. It was first introduced by Dr. Wallich to the Royal Horticultural Society's garden in London where it flowered in 1829. It seems to have been quite common in the wild in

D. williamsonii
Louis Vogelpoel

Dendrobium longicornu
Louis Vogelpoel

earlier times but has always been rather rare in cultivation.

The pseudobulbs are slender, 20-30 cm tall. The dull green leaves are in two rows, rather narrow and soon deciduous. The flowers are solitary or on short inflorescences bearing 2-3 together and often do not expand fully. The sepals and petals are similar, papery white and rather thin. The funnel shaped lip is fringed at the front margin and has a broad, raised central band which is reddish or yellow, sometimes with divergent streaks of the same colour. The lip has a long slender spur at the base.

Warm conditions during the summer months are required by this species, followed by a much cooler winter.

Dendrobium trigonopus
Reichb.f.
(Syn. *D. velutinum* Rolfe)

In some ways this species seems to be somewhat anomalous in this section, particularly for its yellow flowers, but the stems bear the usual brownish hairs particularly in the upper part. It is widely distributed from Burma through northern Thailand, Laos and southwest China at higher elevations but seems to be nowhere common. The earliest plants introduced into cultivation were sent from Burma and flowered first in London in 1887 in the collection of John Day.

D. trigonopus
E.A. Schelpe

Pseudobulbs upright, erect, short but robust, 10-25 cm long, often purplish brown and grooved and bearing only a few leaves at the tips. The 2-3-flowered inflorescences arise at the upper nodes. The flowers are 2-3 cm across, bright yellow, thick and waxy. The sepals are keeled on the back. The lip is almost equally 3-lobed, the side lobes upright, greenish with brown stripes and the midlobe yellow and finely papillose over its surface.

This has come into cultivation again recently and has not proved difficult to grow in intermediate temperature conditions and in good light and high humidity.

Dendrobium scabrilingue Lindl.

A delightfully fragrant orchid from high elevations in the northern parts of Thailand, Burma and Laos which has similarly waxy and long-lasting flowers. However, the sepals and petals are pure white. The 3-lobed lip has a light yellow or orange, papillose midlobe and the erect side lobes are striped with green.

D. scabrilingue
E.A. Schelpe

Dendrobium bellatulum Rolfe

Two very dwarf species of *Dendrobium* complete the selection of species in this section from southeast Asia. They both have a very broad lip, broader than long, on quite large flowers that are produced on squat pseudobulbs only a few cm long. They are found in northern Thailand, above 1300 m, and also in southwest China, sometimes together. *D. bellatulum* also occurs in northeast India, Burma, Laos and Vietnam.

Pseudobulbs clustered, usually erect, thickest at the middle and tapering towards the apex and base, 5-8 cm tall, covered with black hairs. There are few leaves which are greyish green and soon deciduous. The short inflorescences arise at the nodes on the upper part of the stem and bear 1-3 flowers. The sepals and petals are creamy white. The broad lip is bright orange, scarlet in the throat, with 5 keels, 3 of which form a papillose crest along the midlobe.

This species flowers from January to March and the flowers are long-lasting.

D. bellatulum
Louis Vogelpoel

D. christyanum
Louis Vogelpoel

Dendrobium christyanum Reichb.f.
(Syn. *D. margaritaceum* Finet)

Rather similar but usually a taller plant. The flowers are easily distinguished by the white lip which is yellow or red only in the centre and has only 3 keels close together. It flowers during the rainy season from July to September.

D. dearei
E.A. Schelpe

Dendrobium dearei Reichb.f.

This is the best known of the Philippines orchids in the section *Formosae*. It was collected originally from small islands off the coast of Mindanao by a Colonel Deare in whose honour it was named in 1882. Several English orchid nurseries exhibited it when it flowered for the first time in cultivation during the summer of that year.

The pseudobulbs are rather robust and erect, up to 1 m long but usually shorter. The glossy leaves are borne in two rows along the stems and their tubular sheaths are covered with brownish hairs. The inflorescences arise on the upper part of the stems, usually after the leaves have fallen but also with the leaves. The slender racemes bear 3-6 white flowers. The sepals and petals are 2.5-3.5 cm long, the petals broader than the sepals. The 3-lobed lip is about as long as the petals, its midlobe deflexed and wavy at the margin, streaked or suffused with green towards the base. The lip has a long tubular spur.

This is a very rewarding species to grow and it flowers well on mature growths in late spring or early summer. It needs a warm greenhouse with high humidity throughout the year and as much light as possible during the winter months.

Dendrobium sanderae Rolfe

This species was named in honour of the orchid firm of Sander in whose collection it flowered first in England in 1909. It grows in the mountains of northern Luzon at higher elevations than the other two species, above 1300 m, and flowers during the spring. Two forms of this species have been described from this area and differ in the size of their flowers and flowering time. The larger form, which is the most popular in cultivation, is widely known as 'var. *major*'.

The canes are tall and robust, similar to those of *D. dearei*, with two rows of glossy leaves. The inflorescences appear from the nodes all along the stem or just in the upper half, each bearing 6-12 flowers in a slender raceme. The flowers are large, 8-9 cm in diameter and pure white except for the red or purple lines at the base of the lip and on its side lobes.

D. sanderae
Louis Vogelpoel

This species is not so prolific with its flowers when grown in a temperate greenhouse as it is in its native habitat, but it is still a very attractive orchid to grow. Plants grow best in cooler temperatures than the other two species from the Philippines, but need good air movement, high humidity and a dry period during the winter.

D. sanderae var. major
Louis Vogelpoel

D. schuetzei
Louis Vogelpoel

Dendrobium schuetzei Rolfe

This fine species was also first described from cultivated plants that were said to have been brought from the Philippines. Plants are similar to the other two species but usually smaller and found on the island of Mindanao.

The pseudobulbs are short but stout, usually less than 40 cm long, narrow at first above a rounded swollen base and expanded in the upper part. The basal sheaths which do not support leaves are usually hairless. Glossy leaves are borne in the upper parts of the stems with hairy sheaths. The inflorescences are short with 3-5 flowers. The flowers are white and very showy, well rounded with beautiful large petals, up to 4 cm in diameter. The lip is large, tubular at the base, 3-lobed with greenish colour in the throat and on the side lobes.

This species has grown well mounted on a cork oak slab and in a pot. It flowers during the spring or summer and individual flowers last at least 6 weeks. Unfortunately they have no fragrance.

Dendrobium lowii Lindl.

Twelve species in the section *Formosae* can be found in Borneo. *Dendrobium lowii* occurs as an epiphyte on trees on the mountains of Sarawak, usually above 1000 m altitude. It was named by John Lindley after Hugh Low who first discovered it in north Borneo in 1860.

The stems are slender, 25-40 cm long, leafy in the upper half and with brownish black hairs on the leaf sheaths. The inflorescences arise from the upper nodes. They are slender racemes with 4-6 flowers, each 3-5 cm in diameter. The sepals and petals are buff-yellow, the petals undulate and wider than the sepals. The lip is buff yellow, 3-lobed, the side lobes stained with red at the apex and the midlobe bearing 4-6 lines of long hairs which spring from a yellow or crimson base. It has a long, funnel-shaped spur at the rear.

This is a beautiful species which deserves to be more widely grown. It is not difficult in intermediate temperature conditions in a bright and airy greenhouse.

D. lowii
Louis Vogelpoel

Dendrobium spectatissimum
Reichb.f.
(Syn. *D. speciosissimum* Rolfe
D. reticulatum J.J. Smith)

The most beautiful Bornean species, and perhaps the most beautiful in the section *Formosae*, is undoubtedly *D. spectatissimum* which is probably endemic on Mount Kinabalu in Sabah. It was first described in 1877 by Reichenbach from material collected there by Thomas Lobb.

The pseudobulbs are erect, up to 40 cm long, and rather slender. Both the stems and the leaves are covered with blackish hairs. The inflorescences arise near the top of the stems and bear 1-2 flowers which are fragrant and last up to 6 weeks. The flowers are white and papery, each 7-10 cm across. The sepals are keeled on the back.

D. spectatissimum
S. Collenette (Kew collection)

The large, rounded petals are often reflexed at first, becoming flat later. The lip is 3-lobed with a band of red colouration along the centre, becoming yellow towards the apex.

In the wild, this species seems to be rather rare, growing in only a few sites on small *Leptospermum* bushes that are only a few metres high. Many seedlings have been raised at the Royal Botanic Gardens, Kew from a single capsule imported from Sabah some years ago.

Dendrobium parthenium
Reichb.f.
(Syn. *D. sanderianum* Rolfe)

Another slender species in Sabah which has almost pure white flowers with a few purple streaks and markings along the lip.

D. parthenium
Louis Vogelpoel

Chapter 7
Section Spatulata
(formerly known as *Ceratobium*)

These are the 'antelope dendrobiums'. The petals are long and narrow, upright on either side of the shorter dorsal sepal, and usually spirally twisted. The stems are fleshy, cane-like, borne close together in a dense tuft, sometimes up to 2 m long. They are covered with the hairless, sheathing bases of the leaves. The leaves are a bright green colour, and usually elliptic or ovate-elliptic, borne along the stems in two rows. The inflorescences appear near the top of the stem and are arching or upright, usually elongated and bear many flowers.

The flowers are conspicuous and easily recognised by their long twisted petals. Sometimes the sepals are also twisted but they are usually shorter than the petals. The lip is quite different and usually also a different colour from the rest of the flower, three lobed, with entire margins and one or more keels along its upper surface. It usually has a conspicuous spur at the base.

This section comprises some 46 species which are distributed from eastern Java to New Guinea and the Philippines, southwards to northern Australia and eastwards to several of the Pacific islands. Many of the species grow at low altitudes in hot and humid situations, often overhanging rivers and near the seashore.

Dendrobium antennatum Lindl.
(Syn. *D. d'albertisii* Reichb.f.)

This is one of the smaller species in this section but it is widespread in the wild and well known in cultivation. It has been collected from many parts of New Guinea and the Solomon Islands, as well as in northeast Queensland. It is rather variable in the size of the flowers and in the amount of twisting that the petals display. Formerly, the smaller flowered species with less twisted petals were known as *D. d'albertisii*, but there is considerable variation throughout the wide range of *D. antennatum*. Only one variable species is now

D. antennatum
(Kew collection)

recognised, botanically, but *D. d'albertisii* is still recognised as a separate entity for the registration of orchid hybrids.

The plants are usually epiphytic, erect, with a number of stems 15-80 cm tall. The light green leaves are fleshy at first, becoming leathery as they age, borne in two rows along the stems and with greyish sheathing bases. The inflorescences are erect, arising near the top of the stems, sometimes singly but often in groups of 2-5. The flowers are long-lasting and fragrant. They appear white with twisted green or yellowish-green, upright petals. The lip has conspicuous violet veining and a callus of 5 longitudinal keels.

This species has been found over a wide altitudinal range, from sea level to 1200 m, and plants are tolerant of a range of cultural conditions. Because of its relatively small size it is convenient and easy to grow in a bright and humid greenhouse.

D. stratiotes
Louis Vogelpoel

Dendrobium stratiotes Reichb.f. (Syn. *D. strebloceras* Reichb.f. var. *rossianum* Reichb.f.)

This species is one of the most handsome in the section, with large flowers which have a clearly marked lip and contrasting twisted petals. It is almost like a giant form of *D. antennatum*. Its distribution is much more limited than that species, however, and to date it has been collected only from the Moluccas, although there are questionable records from the Sunda Islands, Sulawesi and west New Guinea.

The stems are erect, cane-like, sometimes swollen about the middle, 60-100 cm tall. The leathery leaves are in two rows and articulated at the base to membranous sheaths. The inflorescences are erect, or almost so, bearing 4-8 large flowers. The sepals are white with undulate margins, the twisted petals shining and yellowish green, and the lip

D. antennatum
G. Kennedy (Kew collection)

D. canaliculatum
E.A. Schelpe

white with violet veining on the side lobes or throughout.

This species is much sought after in cultivation and has been widely used in hybridising. In a bright, humid, and bouyant atmosphere it flowers freely, often several times a year. Albino forms are known and were originally described as the var. *rossianum* of *D. strebloceras* which, however, is a different Moluccan species with darker flowers.

Dendrobium canaliculatum
R. Br.
(Syn. *D. tattonianum* Bateman ex Reichb.f.)

This is a small Australian species which has only recently been transferred to section *Spatulata*. Its flower structure clearly indicates its close affinities with other species in this section although vegetatively the plants are rather different. It was first collected along the Endeavour River by Banks and Solander.

The plants are readily recognised by their short pseudobulbous stems bearing a few succulent leaves in a group near the apex. The leaves are a dull greyish green, fleshy, with a shallow groove on the upper surface. The inflorescences are erect, one or several from near the top of each pseudobulb. Each bears many fragrant flowers which, in the best forms, have yellow tipped sepals and petals and a purple lip. There is wide variation in flower colour, however. Some forms have brown or blackish petals and have been called var. *nigrescens*, while others with very pale flowers have been called var. *pallidum*. Some Australian botanists now consider that *D. tattonianum* is the correct name for the form with yellow and purple flowers and that the name *D. canaliculatum* should be applied to the plants with brown flowers.

In Australia and southern New Guinea the plants grow in full sun, very often on trees of the genus *Melaleuca* which are known locally as 'paperbark trees'. The orchid roots grow within the layers of papery bark of these trees. In cultivation the plants need to be grown in strong light and do well if they are kept dry during spells of cooler weather. They easily rot if conditions are cool and humid.

D. canaliculatum
E.A. Schelpe

D. johannis
D.R.M. Stewart

Dendrobium johannis Reichb.f.

This is also an Australian species which extends into southern New Guinea. It is somewhat similar to *D. canaliculatum* but the pseudobulbs are taller with a narrow base and fusiform above. It was named in honour of its discoverer, John Gould Veitch, who sent plants to his father's nursery in England in 1865.

Plants are epiphytic, growing erect and forming slender clumps. The pseudobulbs are swollen in the middle or upper half and bear 3-8 leathery leaves near the apex. The inflorescences are erect or arching racemes with 6-20 chocolate brown flowers.

This species usually flowers in the autumn and grows well in a small pot of well-drained compost or on a slab of cork oak bark. It needs a minimum winter temperature of 10°C and should be kept dry after flowering and throughout the cooler months, but in bright light and a humid atmosphere. In the wild, it is often found on trees growing in or close to swamps. It grows in moister situations than the closely allied *D. trilamellatum* which has larger yellow flowers.

Dendrobium taurinum Lindl.

This attractive orchid occurs on many of the islands in the Philippines and has been known in cultivation for many years. It was first introduced by Hugh Cuming who collected plants for the well known orchid establishment run by the Loddiges family in the early nineteenth century.

The plants are usually epiphytes on low trees in mangrove swamps. The stems are erect, cane-like, 1-3 m or more long and bearing many leaves in two rows. The inflorescences are erect or arching and bear 20-30 large flowers. The white sepals are tinged with green, and the purple or rose-coloured petals are white at the base. The lip is broad and flat, white, heavily flushed with purple or rose in the apical part and purple veined.

This large species needs plenty of space in a warm and humid greenhouse. It flowers freely if conditions are good and has been used extensively to create many floriferous hybrids over the years.

D. taurinum
Jean Dryden

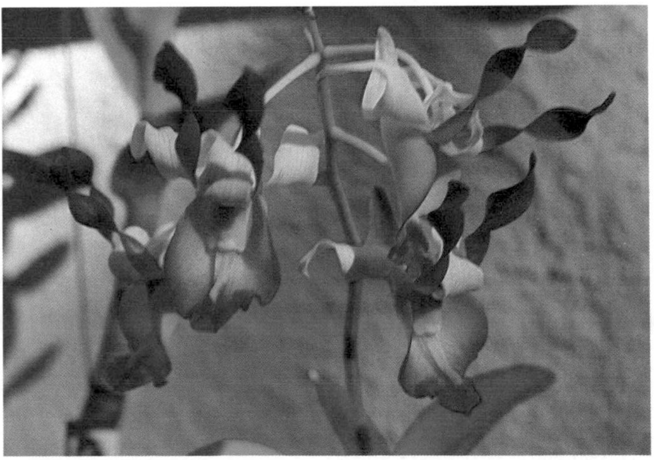

D. discolor
E.A. Schelpe

Dendrobium discolor Lindl.
(Syn. *D. undulatum* R.Br. and *D. broomfieldii* Fitzg.)

This *Dendrobium* is a robust and widespread species in northern Australia and southern New Guinea. It has been widely grown in cultivation for many years, usually under the earlier epithet '*undulatum*' which was used by its discoverer, Robert Brown. Unfortunately this descriptive name, that fits the flowers so well, had been used for another plant by an earlier botanist and must be replaced by the next available name which is *D. discolor*. In the wild, plants often grow on rock outcrops and among boulders, but are also found as epiphytes in scrub and on tall trees.

The pseudobulbs are upright, cane-like, up to 5 m tall. The leathery leaves are borne in two rows. Several erect inflorescences are usually borne near the apex of the stems, each bearing 20-80 flowers. The flowers are very variable in colour and all the parts have convoluted or undulate margins. They are usually creamy yellow or brown, suffused with brown, bronze, or violet. The lip bears a whitish callus. The var. *broomfieldii* differs in having yellow flowers which are variously described as greenish yellow, golden or canary yellow. In all the forms the flowers have a polished, shiny surface.

Many distinct cultivars are grown in tropical gardens where these plants are valued for their free-flowering habit and long-lasting flowers. They form large clumps and often produce 'keikis' from the nodes of old pseudobulbs. These break off and form new colonies. In temperate regions a bright, warm and humid greenhouse is necessary.

Dendrobium helix Cribb

This orchid appears in many different colour forms and it is surprising that it has escaped description and naming until recently. It has been cultivated and used in hybridising over a long period and the forms known as 'Pomio Brown', 'Talasea Lime Yellow' and 'Talasea Mushroom Pink' are well known in the Australian region.

The stems are clustered, cane-like, and up to 2 m or more in height. The leaves are leathery, in two rows along the length of the stems. The inflorescences are erect and grow from the apex of the leafy and leafless stems, carrying 5-20 flowers. The flowers are erect or nodding, yellow, pinkish or brown, sometimes blotched with darker colour and with a maroon or pink central zone on all the parts. The lip also has violet venation and three low ridges along its surface. The petals are characteristically twisted several times.

The plants are usually epiphytic on trees by the seashore and in the forest of coastal regions of New Britain, the only island off New Guinea from which it is known. This species grows easily in cultivation and flowers freely, usually several times a year. It needs bright light in a warm and humid greenhouse.

Dendrobium lasianthera J.J. Smith
(Syn. *D. ostrinoglossum* Rupp)

Many people would say that this is the most spectacular species in the section. It has large rosy purple flowers with darker shiny petals. In the wild, in New Guinea, it grows in swampy forest near sea level and as an epiphyte on small trees near rivers. Andree Millar gave the names 'Sepik Blue' and 'May River Red' to colour forms of this species which she found along the river Sepik and its tributary, the May river.

The clustered canes form large plants with pseudobulbs up to 2.5 m high. Leathery leaves are borne along the upper half of the canes, each articulated to a sheathing base. The erect or arching inflorescences grow up to 60 cm long and bear 8-30 flowers. The showy flowers may be yellowish, variously flushed with purple, but are usually rosy pink with dark maroon petals, while the lip has a whitish mentum.

Plants are sometimes difficult to get established in cultivation, but they thrive in a warm and very humid atmosphere.

Dendrobium tangerinum Cribb

This is one of the prettiest species in the section with its bright yellow or orange red flowers. For a long time it was known to growers quite simply as *Dendrobium* 'Tangerine'. It has also been misidentified, in the past, as *D. strepsiceros*. Phillip Cribb solved the problem of its identity in 1980 when he

D. helix
E.A. Schelpe

D. lasianthera
Joyce Stewart

D. tangerinum
Louis Vogelpoel

described it aâs a new species in *'The Orchid Review'*.

Usually an epiphyte, this species has cane-like pseudobulbs up to 50 cm or more high. The leathery, dark green leaves are articulated to a sheathing base and are borne in two rows along the stem. The inflorescences arise near the apex of the stems, often several together, each bearing 5-15 flowers. The flowers are yellow to orange-brown or orange red with some reddish brown or purplish venation on the sepals. The petals are slightly wider in the upper half and twisted two or three times. The narrow lip bears three lilac ridges and is white at the base.

This New Guinea species grows on rocks as well as trees, usually near the sea but also up to 1250 m inland. The only records from the higher altitudes are of plants which have become established in landslide areas. It flowers freely in cultivation and has been used in hybridising programmes.

Dendrobium mirbelianum Gaud.

This widespread species has been recorded from Queensland and from many of the islands off the northeast coast of Australia and eastern New Guinea. It is rather variable in flower size and some of the smaller flowers are self-pollinating. The plants usually grow as epiphytes in mangroves and forests near the sea, in full sunlight.

The stems are clustered, cane-like, up to 3 m tall but usually smaller. The dark green leaves are borne in two rows, each articulated to a sheathing base and often with purplish stripes on the lower surface. The inflorescences are erect or spreading with 5-30 flowers. The flowers vary in size but are usually olive brown, yellow, or greenish yellow, and the petals are not twisted. The lip is veined with purple brown and has 5 white ridges.

This species is widely grown in cultivation and flowers well. However, it is often mis-labelled *D. schulleri* which is a much rarer species from northwest New Guinea with prettier flowers that are a clear bright yellow.

D. mirbelianum
P.J. Cribb

Chapter 8

Section Phalaenanthe

This section contains the beautiful 'Pompadour' dendrobiums, so-named after some of the hybrids which are widely cultivated for the cut flower market especially in southeast Asia and Hawaii.

The pseudobulbous stems are narrow below and slightly swollen above, appearing spindle shaped when short, or long and cylindric. The lower nodes are covered with sheaths that do not develop leaf blades, while the upper ones bear somewhat leathery, dark-green leaves, with glabrous sheaths. The inflorescences are borne near the apex of the stems, sometimes among the leaves and also on old leafless canes. They are elongated, narrow, erect or arching and usually bear many flowers in the apical half or two thirds.

The flowers are large, purple or white, with the petals much broader than the sepals. The lip is smaller than the petals, three lobed, and decorated with a callus or papillae on its surface. At its base it extends into a blunt mentum.

This section has only a few species which occur in Indonesia, New Guinea and northern Australia.

D. affine in New Guinea

P.J. Cribb

D. affine, white form
(Kew collection)

Dendrobium affine (Decne) Steud.
(Syn. *D. dicuphum* F. Muell.)

It has only recently been determined that the well known Australian orchid, *D. dicuphum*, cannot be separated from the New Guinea species, *D. affine*. Since the latter name was first used several decades earlier than *D. dicuphum*, it has to be accepted. Plants are usually found on paperbark trees overhanging watercourses, and in swampy areas, but they are always subjected to a long dry season.

The plant forms clusters of narrowly fusiform pseudobulbs from 10-50 cm high but usually rather short. Two to ten leaves are borne near the apex of the pseudobulbs and fall off after a few years. The inflorescences arise near the apex of the stems, are erect, and bear up to 60 flowers but usually between 10 and 20. The flowers open wide and flat and all the parts are white or pale pink. The base and side lobes of the lip are often suffused with deep maroon so the flower appears to have a rosy purple centre.

Plants of this species grow best when mounted on a slab of resistant material such as cork oak bark but will also thrive in a small pot. They need good air movement and very bright light. Plants should be watered frequently during the summer months, when they are in active growth, and kept completely dry after flowering and during the cooler, winter season.

D. bigibbum
E.A. Schelpe

Dendrobium bigibbum Lindl.

This name is used here for the smaller forms of the spectacular orchids from the western parts of northern Queensland which are often known as the 'Cooktown Orchids' and which are the floral emblem of that State of Australia. The larger flowered forms are recognised as *D. phalaenopsis* (see below). However, there has been much controversy about the distinctness of these two species and their many varieties and this is continuing, particularly in the Australian literature.

The slender, pseudobulbous stems are often red or purplish, clustered together, usually 40-60 cm long but sometimes reaching 120 cm. There are 10-12 leathery leaves which last for several seasons on the upper part of the stem. The flowers are borne in arching racemes from the apex or upper part of the stem. The rosy purple flowers open wide and flat but often the tips of the sepals and petals are reflexed. White forms are occasionally discovered and pale flowers with a darker lip have also been recorded.

This species grows in semi-arid regions of northern Australia on rocks and as an epiphyte where there is strong light. The plants experience a short hot and humid rainy season and a long dry season at the beginning of which, in autumn, they usually flower. These features of the habitat give some clues to the successful cultivation of this species, which grows rapidly while there is plenty of water and then requires a definite 'rest'. It was recorded in cultivation at Kew in 1824 and has been grown by enthusiasts throughout the world ever since.

Left:
D. bigibbum
Joyce Stewart

Right:
D. phalaenopsis
Louis Vogelpoel

Dendrobium phalaenopsis Fitzg.
(Syn. *D. bigibbum* Lindl. var. *superbum* Hort. ex H.G. Reichb.f.
D. bigibbum Lindl. var. *phalaenopsis* (Fitzg.) Bailey)

This species is very variable but can usually be recognised by its broad, flat flowers, with tepals that do not reflex as in *D. bigibbum* and a more pointed lip. This is the orchid which occurs near Cooktown and along the eastern coast of northern Queensland and also in Indonesia.

The plants are epiphytes or lithophytes with slender, reddish pseudobulbs in clusters up to 120 cm high. The leaves are dark green, often with purplish margins, usually 3-5. The arching racemes bear 2-20 large, rosy purple flowers with broad petals. The lip has straight sides and a sharply pointed tip. It is flushed with a darker purple colour at the base and in the side lobes.

Like *D. bigibbum*, this species requires tropical conditions in cultivation and a definite dry period after flowering. Many beautiful hybrids have been bred by careful selection and hybridising. These seem to be easier to manage in cultivation and grow and flower throughout the year. Bright light, high humidity and good drainage around the roots are essential for good growth.

Dendrobium x superbiens Reichb.f.

This name almost certainly applies to plants which are natural hybrids between *D. bigibbum* and *D. discolor* and which have been in cultivation for at least a century. The petals are much narrower than in *D. bigibbum*, but in cultivation the plants should be treated similarly.

D. x superbiens
Louis Vogelpoel

Dendrobium williamsianum
Reichb.f.

This slender species from Papua New Guinea is not yet widely available in cultivation. It grows in the hot, dry savannah areas where there is a long dry season, usually in the crowns of small trees.

The cane-like stems are upright but very slender, sometimes reaching 3 m long. The midgreen leaves are borne in two rows on the top third of the stem. The inflorescences arise at or near the apex of the stems and form erect or arching racemes each bearing 3-10 flowers. The pale mauve flowers are somewhat nodding and best viewed from below. The broad sepals and petals have a purplish veining and a purple flush towards the base. The lip is a rich dark purple with a paler margin and bears raised, purplish black ridges.

This attractive species needs the same treatment in cultivation as *D. bigibbum*, with a prolonged dry 'rest' after flowering.

D. williamsianum
P.J. Cribb

Chapter 9
Section Latouria

These robust dendrobiums from New Guinea are easily recognised as members of section Latouria, especially those whose flowers are hairy or bristly on the outer surface. In a recent study, Phillip Cribb (1983) recognised 48 species and described and illustrated them. Rather few of the species are in cultivation, however, at least in Europe and America.

The stems may be quite small or robust and up to 60 cm high, arising from a basal rhizome, sometimes close together or spaced along it. The pseudobulbs are narrow at the base and swollen, often angular, above. The leaves are borne near the stem apex and lack sheaths. The inflorescences arise among the leaves and bear several flowers, often drooping so that the flowers are somewhat hidden among the leaves.

The flowers are usually large, white, yellowish or greenish, often with blackish or purplish markings on the inner surface. The sepals and petals are similar, but the sepals and ovary are often covered with bristly hairs. The lip is larger than the other parts of the flower, three lobed with erect side lobes, hairless on its inner surface but bearing a complex white callus near its base.

Most of the orchids in this section occur in New Guinea where there are more than 40 species. A few also occur in adjacent parts of Asia from the Philippines in the north and Java in the west to Fiji and Samoa in the east and southwards to northern Australia.

D. spectabile
E.A. Schelpe

Dendrobium spectabile (Bl.) Miq.
(Syn. *D. tigrinum* Rolfe ex Hemsley)

This spectacular species was first recognised in 1850. It became, in fact, the basis of the name for this section, for Blume originally described it as a member of the genus *Latourea*, a name which is no longer upheld. It is widespread in New Guinea and also occurs in the adjacent islands of Bougainville and the Solomons group. It is an epiphyte in lowland forest, often where conditions are rather swampy, and it also grows well on introduced coconut and *Casuarina* trees. It may be found in the hot and humid areas near sea level and also up to 1100 m inland. It has also been collected from the ground, growing in thick moss and peat, apparently a survivor after falling from trees.

The pseudobulbs are cane-like, gradually thickened upwards from a narrow base, and up to 60 cm tall. Each cane bears 4-6 leathery leaves near the apex; they are bright green when young but become dull and darker as they age. The inflorescences arise from just below the leaf bases and are usually erect or arching outwards away from the leaves. They may be 20-40 cm long and bear few or many spectacular flowers. The flowers are large and somewhat grotesque as each of the tepals is long, pointed and twisted with undulate margins. Basically yellow or greenish, they are heavily spotted with maroon on the sepals and petals while the lip is lined with maroon or purple.

D. macrophyllum
Louis Vogelpoel

In cultivation this species grows well in a warm greenhouse. One plant has grown extremely well planted out in a bed in the Princess of Wales Conservatory at Kew, but others succeed in plastic pots with a fairly open but moisture-retentive compost.

Dendrobium macrophyllum A. Rich.
(Syn. *D. veitchianum* Lindl.
D. ferox Hassk.
D. psyche Kraenzl.
D. musciferum Schtr.)

This widespread species has long been known from several parts of its range between Java and Samoa. It is usually an epiphyte in forests, and occurs from sea level up to 2000 m inland. As might be expected from its wide range, it is extremely variable in flower size and colouration. These are probably the reasons that it has received a large number of names at different times in the past, only the most well known of which are given above. However, it is always easily recognisable, among the other plants with hairy ovaries and sepals, by its normally 3-leaved pseudobulbs.

This is a medium to large size epiphyte with the pseudobulbous stems often reaching 50 cm or more in height and somewhat swollen in the upper half. There are usually three rather leathery light green leaves which are often purple on the lower surface. The inflorescences are long, up to 40 cm, arise among the leaves and bear up to 20 flowers. The pedicels and ovaries and the outer surface of the greenish sepals are covered with bristly hairs. The flowers are creamy white, green or yellowish, with purplish stripes on the lip side lobes and spots or stripes on the mid-lobe.

Dendrobium polysema Schltr.

Rather similar to this species, but differs in having only 2-leaved pseudobulbs.

The hybrid made with *D. atroviolaceum*, *Dendrobium* New Guinea, is more widely cultivated than either of its parents and seems to be easier to grow. All these plants need bright light in a warm and humid greenhouse.

D. polysema
E.A. Schelpe

Dendrobium atroviolaceum Rolfe

This attractive and neat species was one of the earliest in this section to be introduced to cultivation. It is still popular although largely superseded by its more robust hybrid, *Dendrobium* New Guinea (*D. atroviolaceum* x *D. macrophyllum*). It is only known from some of the islands off the southeast of Papua New Guinea where it grows as an epiphyte on rain forest trees from 300-750 m above sea level.

The plants are usually erect, 20-30 cm high, with distinctive pseudobulbs that are very slender below and swollen in the upper half. One or two dark green leaves are borne at the apex and the few flowered inflorescence arises between them. The inflorescence is about 20 cm long and carries up to 20 flowers, each 5 cm across. The flowers are cream, marked with violet, with the lip usually yellow and more heavily marked than the other parts. They are nodding, so that the pretty inner surface is not easily seen, and very long-lasting.

Plants of this species are easily maintained in a warm and humid greenhouse where there is plenty of air movement. It has been a successful parent in several hybrids, notably *D.* Nellie Slade, where the other parent is *D. rhodostictum*, and *D.* New Guinea mentioned above. The hybrids grow vigorously and flower continuously over a long period.

D. atroviolaceum
P.J. Cribb

Dendrobium johnsoniae
F. Muell.
(Syn. *D. macfarlanei* Reichb.f.
D. niveum Rolfe
D. monodon Kraenzl.)

This is one of the prettier orchids in this section of *Dendrobium* with relatively large flowers borne on small tidy plants. It occurs in New Guinea and the Solomon Islands in montane forests between 500 and 1200 m above sea level and especially favours *Casuarina* trees along watercourses.

The fusiform pseudobulbs grow close together, upright, 15-30 cm high, and bear 2-5 leaves at the apex. The leaves are a rather dull green, elliptic or oblong. The inflorescences emerge from among the leaves and bear few to many flowers in a raceme 15-25 cm long. The flowers are large, showy, snow white with purple lines on the inner surface of the side lobes of the lip. The petals are wider than the sepals and all the parts are glabrous.

This attractive orchid is popular in cultivation and has been used as a parent in hybridising in the 1960's. It grows well in a moisture-retentive compost in either a clay or plastic pot kept in a bright and humid greenhouse.

D. johnsoniae
Louis Vogelpoel

D. forbesii
E.A. Schelpe

Dendrobium forbesii Ridl.

This is another white flowered species and one of the most floriferous and attractive in the section. It is known only from eastern New Guinea where it is an epiphyte in montane forest between 900 and 1500 m above sea level.

Plants are robust with pseudobulbous stems up to 30 cm tall. Two rather wide, leathery leaves are borne at the apex of each stem. The erect inflorescence bears 7-20 attractive flowers which are creamy or pure white with some purple streaks on the side lobes of the lip. The flowers have few hairs on the outer surface, but the pedicel and the violet ovary of the flowers is distinctly bristly. The wide petals are a notable feature of the flowers.

This species is rather rare in cultivation but is well worth growing when seedlings become available.

Dendrobium rhodostictum
F. Muell. & Kraenzl.
(Syn. *D. madonnae* Rolfe)

This attractive species grows both as an epiphyte and as a terrestrial plant in Papua New Guinea and the Solomon Islands. It seems able to colonise wet mossy slopes where new roads are built as well as the mossy branches of rain forest trees between 800 and 2000 m above sea level.

The erect stems have very characteristic pseudobulbs which are very slender below and swollen and club shaped, sometimes ovoid, in the upper quarter or third. Two to four dark green leaves are borne near the apex and from among these the erect inflorescence bearing 2-8 flowers emerges. The flowers are large, white and nodding, with conspicuous purple spots on the side margins of the lip.

This species is easily raised from seeds and flowers at a young age on small plants. It grows well in pots in a brightly lit greenhouse with intermediate temperatures.

D. rhodostictum
E.A. Schelpe

Chapter 10
Section Dendrocoryne

The spring-flowering dendrobiums from eastern Australia make up this attractive section.

The stems are pseudobulbous and borne in dense tufts. They may be slender, greatly thickened, or slender near the base and thickened near the apex, upright or pendent. The leaves are dull or dark green, leathery, have no basal sheaths, and are usually borne close together near the apex of the stem. The inflorescences arise among the leaves, or on old leafless pseudobulbs, and usually bear many flowers.

The starry flowers have similar, usually pointed, sepals and petals. The lip is shorter and three lobed, often held away from the column so that the flower appears wide open. There are no hairs on its surface but it may be variously spotted or bear shallow keels.

Dendrobium aemulum R. Br.

First collected by the botanist Robert Brown in the area that is now Sydney, this species was also seen in cultivation in England at an early date, 1824, from plants sent back to Kew by the collector Allan Cunningham from New South Wales. It is now known to be widespread along the eastern side of Australia, usually as an epiphyte and on a variety of different trees. Several different varieties have been recognised, the differences apparently related to the various host trees and types of habitats. Plants usually grow on trunks and branches of trees, often pressed close to the bark.

The pseudobulbs are upright but rather variable, squat and oblong or long and slender to 30 cm, usually dark reddish brown. Two to four dark green leaves are borne apically. The inflorescences are upright or horizontal, with 4-12 creamy white flowers. The petals are much narrower than the sepals and often recurved. The lip is wider and shorter than the other parts with a prominent yellow callus in the centre.

This species is easily grown on hardwood slabs or pieces of cork oak bark. It does well in a greenhouse where there is a pronounced temperature difference between winter and summer,

D. aemulum
E.A. Schelpe

and needs plenty of water during the summer months when new growths are developing. After the plants dry off, the flowers are produced in midwinter.

Dendrobium speciosum Smith

The 'Rock Orchid' is the most widespread of the Australian epiphytic orchids and is also commonly found on rocks. It is distributed from coastal lowlands to high in the rainforests of the eastern mountains where it is frequently found along streams and even in very exposed situations. Its thick pseudobulbs and tough leathery leaves make it instantly recognisable. It was one of the earliest Australian orchids seen in flower in England and flowered at Kew in 1824.

The pseudobulbs form large, thick clumps up to 1 m high with each stem up to 6 cm in diameter, covered in white papery sheaths when young. There are 2-5 large, apical leaves which are thick, leathery and dark green. The arching racemes arise among the leaves or from old leafless pseudobulbs and bear numerous cream or yellowish flowers which vary in size, the largest up to 4.5 cm across. The petals are shorter and narrower than the sepals and the lateral sepals are usually incurved. The lip is much shorter, 3-lobed, usually spotted or streaked with purple.

Five varieties, each with a fairly distinct geographical range, have been described and can be recognised by small differences in their flowers. This is a very variable species but it is very easily grown in a cool greenhouse and flowers well during the winter months. Plants become quite large and do best if they are maintained, undisturbed, in large containers of coarse potting mix.

D. speciosum
E.A. Schelpe

They should be watered and fed regularly during the summer months and allowed to dry off in autumn. They need bright light during the winter to promote flower bud development from the hardened growths.

Dendrobium kingianum Bidw. ex Lindl.

This very well known orchid, which is in almost every collection, is usually a lithophyte in Australia where it is known as the 'Pink Rock Orchid'. It is very variable in the wild and often forms large colonies in suitable open sites. It may be completely exposed to the wind, rain and sun, but also grows well in more sheltered localities up to an altitude of 1200 m.

Plants are made up of tufts of tapering pseudobulbs which are thickest at the base and 6-35 cm tall, often reddish. Two to seven greyish green leaves are borne apically. The inflorescences develop from the apical nodes, often from the same nodes in successive years, each bearing 2-15 flowers. They vary in colour from white, pale to deep pink with darker markings, to reddish purple and are about 2 cm across.

This species is very easy to grow in cool greenhouse conditions, either on a piece of rock, on a bark slab, in a basket, or in a shallow pot of coarse potting mix. It needs plenty of water during the summer and very little during the winter months. Aerial shoots, or 'keikis' tend to develop instead of flowers if the plants are kept too wet during the winter. New plants are

D. kingianum
P.J. Cribb

easily propagated from these keikis.

Several natural hybrids have been recorded and have been introduced into cultivation including **D. x delicatum** (the other parent is *D. speciosum* var. *hillii*), **D. x kestevenii** (the other parent being *D. speciosum*) and **D. x suffusum** (the other parent being *D. gracilicaule*). These are sometimes misidentified as forms of *D. kingianum*.

Dendrobium tetragonum Cunn.

This 'Tree Spider Orchid' is intriguing by its growth habit. New pseudobulbs emerge from the base of a clump in an upward direction but as they grow longer, and their leaves unfurl, they become pendent. They are always slender at the base and swollen and 4-angled, as the name implies, in the upper part. This is another very variable species in which a number of distinct varieties have been recognised by

Left:
D. tetragonum
var. giganteum
D.R.M. Stewart

Right:
D. tetragonum
var. hayesianum
D.R.M. Stewart

their distribution allied to small differences in the flowers. Some Australian botanists consider that they represent distinct but allied species.

Pseudobulbs in pendulous tufts, up to 45 cm long, narrow at the base and 4-angled in the upper third. There are 2-5 broad apical leaves, which are glossy at first, becoming dark green. The inflorescences are apical, up to 3 cm long, bearing 2-5 starry flowers which are rather variable in size and colour. The petals are usually smaller than the sepals and paler in colour. Flowers usually greenish or yellowish with dark reddish brown margins or spots. The lip is cream or yellowish with red spots and streaks and a central white callus of 3 ridges.

Plants of this species are easily maintained in a cool but bright greenhouse. They should be attached when small to a piece of cork oak bark or slab of wood. They need good air movement and a dry period during the winter to produce their flowers in spring.

Chapter 11
Section Pedilonum

This group of 20-30 species is characterised by the few or many-flowered inflorescences arising on leafless stems.

The fleshy stems are pendent or upright and may be short or rather elongated. The leaves are evenly spaced along their length and all have sheaths enclosing the stem below each node. The inflorescences usually arise from the nodes, not always near the apex of the leafless stems, and are rather short, with few or many flowers.

The flowers are brightly coloured, often pink, red or purplish. The lateral sepals are broader and usually joined together at the base on the lower side. The lip is long and narrow with its basal spur tucked inside the connate lateral sepals.

This section is primarily a New Guinea one, but its circumscription has been broadened recently to include plants from Malaysia, Thailand and Indonesia which were formerly separated into section *Calcarifera*. Nineteen species are recorded from Borneo. Some species, e.g. *D. smilliae*, seem very close to section *Calyptrochilus* and further study may reveal that some changes should be made to the allocation of species to these two sections.

Dendrobium amethystoglossum
Reichb.f.

This attractive species comes from mountainous areas in the Philippines where it grows on limestone cliffs. Although it is rather rarely seen in cultivation, it is highly prized for its floriferous habit and the long-lasting bunches of flowers which appear during the winter months.

The cane-like stems are usually upright and may reach a length of 50-90 cm. The leaves are soft and light green and usually fall off after one season before the flowers are produced. The inflorescences are short and pendent, usually several on each stem, with 15-20 flowers in a dense cluster. Individually the flowers are large for the section, up to 3 cm across, and white with an amethyst purple lip.

D. amethysto-glossum
Louis Vogelpoel

This species was first introduced to Europe by Gustav Wallis for the firm of Veitch and described by Reichenbach soon afterwards. It grows well in cool or intermediate conditions in the greenhouse where there is plenty of air movement and good drainage around the roots.

Dendrobium victoriae-reginae Loher

This species was dedicated to Queen Victoria by its discoverer, A. Loher, who described it in 1897. It almost disappeared from cultivation but plants have become available from the Philippines again recently and the species has been propagated from seeds. The attractive, almost blue flowers appear during the spring and summer months.

Stems upright or pendent, often swollen at the nodes, usually 15-40 cm long, and bearing light green leaves which are soon deciduous. The inflorescences are short, close to the stem, and usually bear 2-5 rather shiny flowers, rarely up to 12. The sepals and petals are white near the base but the whole of the upper part is a pretty violet blue. The lip is orange yellow near the base and violet blue towards the apex.

Cool mossy forests at high altitudes are the native habitat of this attractive species. In cultivation it needs cool treatment and can be well watered throughout the year provided there is good drainage around the roots.

Dendrobium miyakei Schltr.

An attractive orchid in Taiwan which has sometimes been treated as a variety of *D. victoriae-reginae*. The plants are similar or larger but the flowers are smaller, 1-1.5

D. victoriae-reginae
Joyce Stewart

Left:
D. miyakei
E.A. Schelpe

Right:
D. secundum
E.A. Schelpe

cm across, and a rich, purplish red colour. It is usually grown in an intermediate greenhouse, in semi-shade, and needs a cool dry winter.

Dendrobium secundum (Blume) Lindl.

This widespread species has a large number of different colour forms, some more attractive than others. It occurs throughout the Malaysian region, from Burma southeastwards to Indonesia and the Philippines. It is a common plant in forests where there is a pronounced dry season.

The slender, cane-like stems may be upright but usually become pendent with age and reach a length of 25-120 cm depending on the growing conditions. The leaves are light green, borne in two rows and may persist for more than one season. The inflorescences arise from the upper nodes of the stems and are short and dense with many flowers. The flowers are often arranged so that they all face one side (i.e. they are secund) and are thick and waxy, white, cream, pink or purplish red with an orange or yellow lip.

This species is easily cultivated in an intermediate greenhouse and grows best in a small pot which has good drainage or mounted on a slab of cork oak bark. The flowers appear during the winter months, when the plants are kept dry, and are long-lasting.

Dendrobium bracteosum Reichb.f.

This species also occurs in a number of different colour forms, but the flowers are often somewhat hidden by the large bracts after which the species is named. It is common in the mountains of Papua New Guinea and also in the forests down to sea level.

The stems are usually short and stubby making rather compact plants 20-40 cm high. The thin leaves are borne in two rows but are soon deciduous. The inflorescences appear at the nodes

D. bracteosum
Louis Vogelpoel

of leafless stems, often from the same point for many years. The flowers are in tight clusters and may last up to six months. The colour varies from white to cream, pale or dark pink and a rich rosy red. The pointed lip is yellow or orange.

This species is not difficult to grow in warm or intermediate conditions in the greenhouse and the richer coloured forms are particularly welcome.

Dendrobium capituliflorum Rolfe

This is another lowland species from New Guinea which is a forest epiphyte, but it is not so often seen in cultivation.

The pseudobulbs are usually erect, constricted just above the base and then widening to rather fleshy stems of several nodes and reaching 10-25 cm long. The leaves are rather dark, especially on the upper surface, and purplish underneath. The inflorescences are borne on the leafless pseudobulbs, and the flowers appear to grow in tight clusters. Each small flower is rather elongated with a distinct mentum or spur. It is white or cream, tinged with green, and the lip is a bright apple green in its lower parts.

With good drainage this species grows well in a clay or plastic pot in a warm and humid greenhouse. It also does well when mounted on a slab of durable material such as cork oak bark.

Left:
D. bracteosum
Louis Vogelpoel

Right:
D. capituliflorum
E.A. Schelpe

With Compliments

SIMON FAVELL INDUSTRIES LTD.
CONSTRUCTION DIVISION

P.O. Box 29
31 Penmore Gardens
Hasland
Chesterfield
S41 0TZ
Telephone: (0246) 271523
Mobile Phone: 0831 292860

Dendrobium bullenianum Reichb.f.
(Syn. *D. topaziacum* Ames)

This species first became known from a plant in cultivation which was imported by the orchid nursery of Messrs Low from the Philippines. It has been widely grown under the much later name of *D. topaziacum*.

The pseudobulbs are long and slender, upright or pendent, often grooved longitudinally, up to 60 cm long. The thin leaves are borne in two rows but are not long-lasting. The inflorescences appear from the nodes of leafless stems and carry dense clusters of bright orange red flowers. The flowers are rather long and narrow with the lip extending into a conspicuous broad spur.

This is a very attractive species in cultivation and is not difficult in an intermediate greenhouse.

D. bullenianum
E.A. Schelpe

Dendrobium smillieae F. Muell.
(Syn. *D. ophioglossum* Reichb.f.)

This robust species grows both in New Guinea and in the tropical parts of northern Australia. It grows at sea level and up to medium altitudes, usually in shaded positions. In Australia it is sometimes known as the 'Bottlebrush orchid'. Perhaps it would be more correctly placed in section *Calyptrochilus*.

Many stems grow together to form large clumps, but the stems are slender, erect, 15-100 cm long. The thin leaves are soon deciduous. The inflorescences appear from the nodes towards the apex of the leafless stems and carry many flowers in a short dense raceme. The flowers are white, cream, or pink, while the resupinate lip has a bright green shiny, hooded apex. With the lateral sepal it forms, at its base, an elongated nectary. Sometimes the tips of all the floral parts are pale green.

D. smillieae
Louis Vogelpoel

In culture this species does well mounted on a suitable slab but it can also be grown in a pot of well drained compost. During the summer months the new growth develops quickly and the plants need plenty of moisture. This is followed by a dry period when growth is complete. More light is needed after the leaves have fallen to encourage flowering.

D. chrysoglossum
E.A. Schelpe

Dendrobium chrysoglossum Schltr.

A rather similar orchid that is found at higher altitudes in New Guinea. The flowers are borne in several tight clusters, usually near the apex of the pseudobulb. The sepals and petals are a pale rose pink and the lip is bright orange, arching around the white or yellow column.

Dendrobium cumulatum Lindl.

The specific name refers to the crowded inflorescences. This species was introduced to cultivation from Burma several times in the last century, but no longer seems to be widely grown. It is also widespread in India, Nepal, Sikkim and Bhutan between 300 and 1000 m.

The stems are tufted and slender, usually pendulous, 45-60 cm long. The pointed leaves are light green and soon deciduous. The flowers are borne in dense inflorescences, each one made up of many flowers, 2-3 cm across. The sepals and petals are pale rosy purple, more or less equal. The lip is longer and broader than the petals, prolonged at its base into a curved spur.

This species thrives when mounted on a block of tree fern fibre or in a small basket. It needs a dry and cool winter after a warm and humid growing period during the summer.

D. cumulatum
Louis Vogelpoel

Chapter 12
Section Calyptrochilus
(including section *Glomerata*)

The brightly coloured species in this section have very tough and thick flowers which are bird pollinated.

The fleshy stems are erect or pendent, rather slender, 50-100 cm long in mature plants. The leaves all have sheathing bases and are uniformly spaced along the stems, usually arranged so that they appear in two rows on either side of the stem. Inflorescences arise from the upper part of the stems, usually after the leaves have fallen. They are short, with few or many flowers close together.

Flowers bright red, pink, purplish, orange or yellow, very thick and almost waxy, long-lasting. The lateral sepals form an elongated mentum around the extended column foot so that the whole flower looks very long and narrow. The apex of the lip is incurved or hooded with a fringed margin.

This section is centred on New Guinea where there are more than 60 species. Some of these also occur in the islands of the western Pacific Ocean.

Dendrobium subclausum Rolfe
(Syn. *D. phlox* Schltr.)

This epiphyte is common in the undisturbed forests of New Guinea between 600 and 900 m altitude and has also been collected much higher up, between 1200 and 2500 m, growing as a terrestrial plant on rocks and clay cliffs. Its habit of growth and flower colour are both rather variable.

Stems upright or pendent, slender, often branched, covered with fine warts on the leaf sheaths, 50-100 cm long. The leaves are light green, arranged in two rows along the whole length of the stems. The inflorescences arise from various nodes on the leafless stems, apparently haphazardly, over many years from the same

D. subclausum
Louis Vogelpoel

dry stem. The flowers are in short racemes of 2-10 and appear tubular, each about 2 cm long. They are pale yellow, gold or orange with a darker mentum. Sometimes the sepals and petals are orange tipped.

This species grows easily but rather untidily in a cool or intermediate greenhouse. There is a rather similar species in the Solomon Islands, **D. mohlianum** Reichb.f.

D. mohlianum
Louis Vogelpoel

Dendrobium lawesii F. Muell.

This is one of the best known of the New Guinea orchids and has become much sought after by orchid growers. Fortunately it has proved to be easily propagated from seeds. It is epiphytic throughout a wide range of altitudes in mountainous parts of New Guinea, from 650 to 1200 m above sea level. It has also been collected in the Solomon Islands.

D. lawesii
E.A. Schelpe

The pseudobulbs grow in pendulous clusters from the undersides of branches. The curving stems are 25-50 cm long, usually purplish brown. The leaves form two neat rows on either side of each stem and are dark green, sometimes with a purplish midrib. The inflorescences arise on both leafy and leafless stems, but are more frequent on the latter. Each short raceme bears a cluster of 5-8 bell shaped flowers. They are 2-5 cm long and only about 1-1.5 cm across the expanded part of the tepals. The flowers vary in colour from a clear pink to red, cerise and purple, sometimes with white tips to deep orange, yellowish or rarely white. They are thick and waxy and last on the plant for several months throughout the winter flowering period.

Plants of this species are easily maintained in cultivation either in a small pot of well drained compost or mounted on a durable medium such as a cork oak slab. Plenty of air movement, combined with a humid atmosphere throughout the year ensure healthy growth.

Chapter 13
Section Oxyglossum
(including section *Cuthbertsonia*)

These are delightful miniature orchids which mostly have large and brightly coloured flowers. This section is immediately recognised by the winged or ribbed ovaries behind the flower.

Small tufted plants with short stems borne very close together. There are rather few leaves, with sheathing bases, on the upper parts of the stems. The inflorescences arise near the apex of the stems and bear 1-4 flowers.

The flowers are brightly coloured and often appear rather flattened especially when seen from below. Sepals and petals rather similar. The lip is boat shaped and tightly attached to the column foot for most of its length. It fits inside a spur-like projection made by the fused basal part of the lateral sepals.

These desirable species occur in the highlands of New Guinea and a few species have been recorded in Indonesia and some of the islands of the Pacific as far east as Fiji. They are mostly montane species, occurring at high elevations in the cloud forest and mist zones with their roots amongst permanently moist mosses. They are best mounted on cork oak slabs or chunks of tree fern fibre in cultivation. Some growers have been successful with potted plants, especially those raised from seeds.

Dendrobium cuthbertsonii
F. Muell.
(Syn. *D. sophronites* Schltr.
D. agathodaemonis J.J. Smith
D. fulgidum Ridley)

This delightful gem of an orchid has become widely known in cultivation over the last 25 years as *D. sophronites*, a name given to it by Schlechter in allusion to the red flowers which are superficially similar to those of the Brazilian orchid genus, *Sophronitis*. However, a study of many plants in New Guinea and in herbaria has shown that this is a very variable orchid, both in the shape and size of the plants and the colour of the flowers, and that this and many other synonyms refer to the plant which is correctly known as *D. cuthbertsonii*. In the wild the plants are usually epiphytes, on trees, shrubs and tree ferns, occasionally terrestrial or on rocks near streams, road cuttings and on exposed cliff faces. They usually grow in semi-shade but where there is good air movement. This species occurs throughout the mountains of New Guinea, from c. 750-3450 m altitude.

This is a clump-forming plant with short, ovoid pseudobulbs up to 8 cm long arising close to each other from a basal rhizome which is often hidden in the surrounding moss. The leaves are few or solitary, borne near the apex of the pseudobulbs, dull greyish green or purplish and covered with shiny papillae or warts. The flowers are borne singly and are up to 5 cm in diameter, commonly red, but also orange, purple, pink, yellow or white with an orange lip which is uppermost in the flower because the slender pedicel is rather weak and the flower is nodding.

These plants grow best when established on a block of soft tree fern fibre and kept under cool, semi-shaded conditions. They need misting over several times a day, especially during the summer months, provided there is good air movement. They have no definite flowering season and individual flowers have been recorded lasting as much as 8 months.

Dendrobium violaceum Kraenzl.
(Syn. *D. dryadum* Schltr.
D. quinquecostatum Schltr.)

This is one of the more widespread species of this section in New Guinea. Its distinctive leaves, which are usually long and linear and arise near the top of each pseudobulb, help to identify this species even when it is not in flower. It is one of the largest of the 'oxyglossums' with large and attractive flowers which are recorded as lasting for at least six months. It is almost always an epiphyte on forest margins and in low secondary forest and has been found between 750 and 2000 m altitude.

Stems erect and close together forming tufts of fusiform or ovoid pseudobulbs 1-5 cm long. The pale green leaves are narrow, usually 3 borne together near the apex of the young stems, 5-30 cm long. The inflorescences arise from the upper part of leafless stems and carry 1-4 flowers. The flowers open wide but have a very flattened appearance, up to 3 cm long. They vary in colour with sepals and petals pink to deep violet, sometimes with blue tips, rarely all blue or white. The lip is dark purple with an orange or red apex.

This species is sometimes difficult to establish but when grown from seeds the young plants adapt to greenhouse conditions more easily. In the wild they are found in exposed situations, so should be given plenty of light and good air movement in the greenhouse.

Opposite:
D. cuthbertsonii
Louis Vogelpoel

D. violaceum
E.A. Schelpe

Dendrobium vexillarius
J.J. Smith

This is the most common of all the *Oxyglossum* species in New Guinea and has a wide range of colour forms throughout many different habitats. It can be found as an epiphyte or terrestrial in montane and alpine forests, cloud forests and grasslands between c.1000 and 3500 m. Six different varieties have been recognised in different parts of the range of this species and they are easily distinguished by their flower colour as well as other features.

The plants form tufts of pseudobulbs that may be 1-30 cm high, usually rather short. The narrow leaves are erect or spreading, dark green, 2-10 towards the apex of each stem. The inflorescences arise towards the apex of old and leafy stems and bear 2-5 flowers which appear to be laterally compressed though opening wide to c. 4.5 cm across. The flowers may be red, orange, yellow, whitish, greenish, blue, violet, lilac, pink or purple, with a lip that is green to almost black but with a bright orange or red apex.

These colourful plants have not proved easy to grow in cultivation, but if they do so the flowers are rewarding for up to 6 months. Several plants have been cultivated with great success at the Royal Botanic Garden, Edinburgh and seedlings from some of these are now available.

D. vexillarius
Joyce Stewart

Chapter 14
Section Rhizobium

Plants in this section have thick, fleshy leaves of various shapes, some slender and terete, others flattened and succulent.

Stems wiry, branched and hanging, or forming a dense mat-like growth over rocks or bark. Each branch terminates in a single leathery or fleshy leaf which has no sheath. Inflorescences arising below the terminal leaf and bearing 1-several flowers.

Flowers greenish, white or yellowish, sometimes with reddish markings.

This section is well known in Australia and extends into New Guinea. There is such wide variation in plant form within the section that its exact circumscription is still the subject of discussion.

Dendrobium linguiforme Sw.

The 'Tongue Orchid' is very widespread in eastern Australia and always easily recognised by its tongue shaped leaves which also have a rasping surface, rather like a tongue. It has been known in cultivation for almost two hundred years and is still welcome today both for its curiously shaped leaves, its ease of cultivation, and its attractive white flowers in winter or early spring.

The branching rhizome is tough and creeping, bearing oval or tongue-shaped leaves along its length. The leaves are greyish green or dark green and may have purple blotches when the plants are growing in full sun. The inflorescences are upright, to 15 cm long, and bear up to 20 white or cream flowers which are fragrant. The sepals and petals are narrow and much longer than the broad lip which has 3 purplish ridges.

This species grows in the wild in many different habitats, on rocks in full sun, on trees in rather open forests and also in fairly dense shade. It is widely dispersed

D. linguiforme
D.R.M. Stewart

along the eastern side of Australia from southeastern New South Wales to northeast Queensland. It seems to be very drought resistant and is fairly easy to maintain in cultivation. It does well mounted on a suitable slab and requires good light, humidity and air movement.

Dendrobium teretifolium R. Br.

The 'Pencil Orchid' has attractive fragrant flowers but a rather untidy growth habit. It was described by Robert Brown in 1810 after he discovered it in the region that is now Sydney. However, to the north and south it can still be found, often near the coast but also inland, on *Casuarina* trees and on rocks. It is often near rivers, on trees at the edge of swamps, and along the coastal flats.

The wiry branching rhizomes form tangled mats hanging down from the branches or rocks on which it grows. The stems bear long, terete leaves like narrow pencils. The inflorescences are erect or arching and bear 5-16 white flowers. All the sepals and petals are very narrow, but up to 4 cm long. The lip is white, spotted with red or purple, and the mid-lobe is curved with a long narrow point.

This species flowers during the winter months, sometimes for a month or more. It is very easy to maintain in cultivation in a basket or mounted on a slab of bark. It needs regular watering and feeding during the summer growing season, alternating with a cooler, dry season with bright light to initiate flowering.

D. teretifolium
D.R.M. Stewart

Chapter 15
Section Rhopalanthe

This section includes the well known 'Pigeon Orchid' which is common in cultivation in tropical regions.

The stems in this section are very characteristic. They are thin and almost wiry in the lowermost and upper portions, with several swollen internodes occupying a section in the lower third of their length. With age they often become very long, up to 1 m, and pendent. The leaves are fleshy and confined to the middle of the stem, the base and apical parts bearing only sheaths. The inflorescences are very short, borne at the nodes of the apical, leafless part of the stem, and bear numerous short-lived flowers.

The small or medium sized flowers have similar sepals and petals. The lip is as long as the petals, 3-lobed, and bears a prominent callus on its surface.

The species in this section are found primarily in the Indonesia-Malaysian region, but some extend westwards into the Himalayas. Twenty species are recorded in Borneo.

Dendrobium crumenatum Sw.

The 'Pigeon Orchid' is widely distributed from India eastwards to southern China and southwards throughout the Malaysian region to the Philippines. It flowers as a response to a sudden fall of temperature, often caused by a violent rainstorm. If the temperature drops by 10°F, the flower buds start to develop and exactly nine days later all the pigeon orchid plants in the vicinity of the storm will burst into flower. Furthermore, they are fragrant and many will be pollinated within a few hours of opening. By the afternoon they have faded. This flowering habit can be brought about artificially in the greenhouse by temperature manipulation.

The stems arise close together and are constricted into a narrow base for several nodes. Above this point there are several swollen

D. crumenatum
Louis Vogelpoel

D. cinnabarinum
E.A. Schelpe

nodes before the stem narrows again to a long slender leaf-bearing portion. Above the leaves there is a further slender part which is covered with sheaths where the inflorescences arise from the nodes. The whole stem is 1 m or more long. The flowers are white or greenish, sometimes suffused with pink, with a yellow blotch on the surface of the ridged lip.

Although it does not flower often, this species is an interesting addition to a collection of dendrobiums because of its curious growth habit and because, with care, flowering can be initiated at will. It requires a warm and humid atmosphere in which to grow well and watering throughout the year.

D. cinnabarinum
Louis Vogelpoel

Dendrobium cinnabarinum Reichb.f.

This is often a terrestrial orchid in Sabah but has also been collected from trees.

The stems are long, with an extensive leafy part above the swollen nodes near the base. The leafy part and the inflorescences are often branched and numerous 'keikis' also appear from the upper parts. The brilliantly coloured flowers arise near the tops of the stems and are extremely variable. Several different varieties have been named, based on flower shape and colour. They may be deep orange, cinnabar-red, crimson, or deep pinkish purple with a very narrow lip.

The **var. angustipetalum** Carr has larger flowers with narrower parts than the typical forms and a conical spur at the base of the lip.

Chapter 16
Section Aporum

This section is easily recognised by the stems and leaves being strongly flattened, laterally, so that they resemble the genus *Oberonia*.

The leaves are evergreen, thick and fleshy, arranged in two regularly alternating rows, each one articulated at the base. The inflorescences appear to arise in the leaf axil, towards the apex of the stems, or from the nodes after the leaves have fallen.

The flowers are borne in short racemes from a cluster of chaffy bracts. They are small, yellowish or greenish.

This section is centred in Burma where there are about 25 species. Other species are found in Malaysia, Indonesia, and Borneo.

Dendrobium leonis (Lindl.) Reichb.f.

This species is widespread in the Malaysian region. It is a common epiphyte throughout lowland Malaya, Thailand, Laos, Vietnam and Cambodia, and also occurs in Borneo and Sumatra.

Plants are usually pendent below the branches of forest trees. The stems are straight and reach 25 cm in length. The leaves are spreading and easily recognised by their shape, the lower edge straight and the upper edge curved in a quadrant of a circle. The inflorescences are few-flowered and arise in the axils of the upper leaves. The flowers are small but very fragrant, greenish, sometimes flushed with purple on the outside. The lip has a papillose area on its surface with a purplish spot just below.

This species is easily maintained in a warm greenhouse, either mounted on a piece of cork oak bark or in a small pot.

D. leonis
Louis Vogelpoel

Chapter 17
Section Macrocladium

This is a curious section of plants from New Caledonia where most of the species are terrestrial. They are large branching plants which have been described as 'bamboo-like'.

The stems are wiry, greatly elongated and branched. The leaves are narrow, alternately arranged in two ranks throughout the growth of the plant. The flowers are solitary or in few flowered inflorescences on the youngest growths. The sepals and petals are similar, the lip 3-lobed with distinctive side lobes and several ridges along its surface.

In addition to the New Caledonia species there is one epiphytic species, *D. cunninghamii* Schltr., in New Zealand.

Dendrobium cunninghamii Schltr.

This species is only known in New Zealand but is widely distributed there from the North Island south to Stewart Island. It has the distinction of being the southernmost *Dendrobium* on record. It is found throughout the forested areas but is more common in the lowlands. In coastal districts this species is also found on cliffs, rocks and sometimes on the forest floor. It is named in honour of Allan Cunningham, a botanist from Kew, who was an early botanical explorer of the islands.

D. cunninghamii
David Menzies (Kew collection)

The stems are long, branched and rather woody, often more than 1 m long. The leaves are narrow, yellowish green. The flowers are solitary or borne in short inflorescences of 2-6, each flower 2-4 cm across. The sepals and petals are white or cream, with sparkling texture, reflexed at the tips. The lip has a large cordate, white midlobe, and short erect, rose-red side lobes. There are several ridges on the surface of the lip and a yellowish patch between the side lobes.

This species seems to present no problems in cultivation but is not often seen, at least in Europe. Some large plants at Kew have been growing in a cool greenhouse for many years and flower regularly every summer. They are kept moist throughout the year.

Chapter 18
Section Stachyobium

This section seems to be restricted to Asia.

The plants are mostly rather small and have very thin leaves which often fall off before the plants flower. The inflorescences are usually slender, appearing at one or more of the nodes of the rather short pseudobulbs. Some of the species have curious fimbriae, like the teeth of a comb, along the front edge of the lip.

Like many other Thailand species these benefit from a cooler winter with less water. The summer growing period is usually rather short and sudden.

Dendrobium delacourii Guill.
(Syn. *D. ciliatum* Parish ex Hook.f. var. *breve* Reichb.f.)

This species is quite common in Thailand where it grows in deciduous forests in full sun. In the past it has not always been separated from the much taller and more slender **D. venustum** Teijsm. & Binnend. (syn. *D. ciliatum* Parish ex Hook.f.) which has similar flowers. Both species are also known in Burma, Laos and Vietnam.

The stems are short and squat pseudobulbs, 3-6 cm high. The leaves are light green and soon fall off. The flowers are borne on the young pseudobulbs, before they are fully expanded, and usually emerge between the leaves. The inflorescences bear 8-10 greenish white or pale yellow flowers, each one about 1 cm long. The flowers often do not open fully. The sepals and petals are narrow, the lip 3-lobed. The midlobe is rather short and with conspicuous fat fimbriae along its apical margin. It is produced into a conspicuous mentum at the back.

This species grows easily in cultivation with other Thailand species.

D. delacourii
Louis Vogelpoel

Chapter 19
Section Fytchianthe

This is a small group of species which become completely deciduous before they produce their flowers. The erect inflorescences are produced from near the top of the upright pseudobulbs.

The flowers are very pretty, with wide petals and a conspicuous lip which is broad and flat, hairy towards the base.

This section is represented in India, Sri Lanka and Burma.

Dendrobium fytchianum
Bateman

This has been described as a very elegant little *Dendrobium* which is often picked when it is in flower to use as a hair ornament by people living along the Salween river in Burma. The rosy-eyed, pure white flower is certainly decorative. It was introduced to cultivation by the Rev. Charles Parish. Colonel Fytch was with him at the time of its discovery on a branch overhanging a stream.

The stems are slender, cylindrical, erect, 30-45 cm long. The leaves are light green and only present on the youngest pseudobulbs. The inflorescences arise on leafless stems and are erect, each bearing 8-10 flowers, 3-5 cm across. The sepals are narrow and the petals roundish obovate, the lip 3-lobed. The small incurved side lobes are rose coloured; the obcordate midlobe about as large as the petals, hairy at the base. A pink form of this species, with crimson purple side lobes of the lip and purplish hairs, is also recorded.

This species grows in exposed positions on trees and bushes. It grows well in a small pot or basket in a brightly lit position in a humid greenhouse.

D. fytchianum
E.A. Schelpe

Dendrobium barbatulum
Lindl.

Somewhat similar and has sometimes been confused with *D. fytchianum*. However, this species is entirely pure white or rosy pink, with narrower, pointed petals and bright yellow hairs at the base of the lip. It is only recorded in southern India and in the hills near Bombay, and flowers in spring.

Chapter 20
Section Breviflores

This small section was first proposed by Sir Joseph Hooker for three small orchids from India. Since then other species from a wider area in Asia have been added to it. Its exact circumscription and validity have sometimes been questioned, but we have followed Seidenfaden (1985) in maintaining it for the plants we know.

The stems are usually rather slender, sometimes swollen in the upper part, up to 60 cm long but usually shorter. The leaves are narrow and soon deciduous. The inflorescences are produced along the stems from the nodes in short racemes of 3-10 flowers which are pink, lilac or yellow, sometimes rather dingy. They are chiefly distinguished by the broad, saccate lip which is very short, almost urn shaped with a narrow entrance, sometimes ciliate along the front margin.

These species mostly occur where there is a pronounced dry season alternating with a very warm wet one. As soon as they become leafless, plants in cultivation should be moved to a cooler and dry position in a warm greenhouse.

Dendrobium aduncum Wall. ex Lindl.

This charming species was first introduced from India and subsequently from Malaya and southwest China. It has been in cultivation for more than a century. The specific name probably refers to the hook-like feature at the front of the lip.

The stems are slender and usually pendent, 40-60 cm long. The pointed leaves are soon deciduous. The attractive flowers are 1-2.5 cm across, pale pink with a bright purple anther cap. The sepals and petals are rather similar, the sepals more pointed than the petals. The small, rounded lip is hairy within and has a large, central glossy callus. The lip has a short, hooked apex.

This species grows best mounted on a block of tree fern fibre and needs plenty of water and fertiliser during the growing season. The flowers are borne on the old stems, usually in the spring.

D. aduncum
E.A. Schelpe

Further Reading

Many general books on orchids contain information on dendrobiums and their culture but this is usually limited to some of the species we have described. For additional information one must turn to the floras of parts of the area and to taxonomic works on the sections of *Dendrobium* which are much more complete and informative. We are eagerly awaiting the new edition of the *'Orchids of Malaya'* which has been prepared by Jeffrey Wood and Gunnar Seidenfaden and the *'Orchids of Borneo'* which is also in preparation at Kew. We recommend the following books and publications which are currently available.

Backer, C.A. and R.C. Bakhuizen van den Brink, 1968. *Flora of Java, Volume III.* Groningen, The Netherlands.

Blaxell, D.F., H.J. Katz and J.T. Simmons, 1982. *The Orchidaceae of German New Guinea.* (Translation of the German text of R. Schlechter, 1914, Die Orchidaceen von Deutsch-Neu-Guinea). The Australian Orchid Foundation, Essendon, Victoria.

Cribb, P.J., 1983. A revision of Dendrobium sect. Latouria (Orchidaceae). *Kew Bulletin* 38: 229-306. Also available as a reprint with the same title.

Cribb, P.J., 1986. A revision of Dendrobium sect. Spatulata (Orchidaceae). *Kew Bulletin* 41: 615-692. Also available as a reprint entitled *'The "Antelope" Dendrobiums'*.

These two important papers have been reprinted together by Kew recently, under the title *'A Revision of the Antelope and "Latourea" Dendrobiums'*

Deva, S. and H.B. Naithani, 1986. *The Orchid Flora of Northwest Himalaya*. New Delhi.

Grant, B., 1895. *The Orchids of Burma*. Rangoon. (reprinted 1966).

Karasawa, K., 1988. *Orchid Atlas, Volume 4.* Tokyo.

Lewis, B. and P. Cribb, 1989. *Orchids of Vanuatu*. Royal Botanic Gardens, Kew.

Pradhan, U.C., 1979. *Indian Orchids: Guide to Identification and Culture. Volume II.* Kalimpong.

Reeve, T.M. and P.J.B. Woods, 1989. A revision of *Dendrobium* Section *Oxyglossum* (Orchidaceae). *Notes from the Royal Botanic Garden, Edinburgh* 46: 161-305

Seidenfaden, G., 1985. Orchid Genera in Thailand XII. *Dendrobium* Sw. *Opera Botanica* 83. Copenhagen.

Tsan-Piao Lin, 1975. *Native Orchids of Taiwan. I.* Taiwan.
Upton, W.T., 1989. *Dendrobium Orchids of Australia.* Houghton Mifflin, Australia.
Valmayor, H.L., 1984. *Orchidiana Philippiana. Volume II.* Manila.
Veitch, J., 1888. *A Manual of Orchidaceous Plants. Part III. Dendrobium.* London. (Reprint by A. Asher and Co., Amsterdam, 1965).

Publications on Dendrobium by E.A. Schelpe

Ted Schelpe published many papers, review articles and several books on the orchids of South Africa as well as many articles on a wide variety of cultivated orchids. The papers on *Dendrobium* that we have traced include the folowing:

1970 Some trends in the breeding of *Dendrobium nobile* hybrids. *South African Orchid Journal,* Vol.1 (3): 19-22

1980 The distribution of some cultivated species of *Dendrobium*. *South African Orchid Journal,* Vol. 11 (1): 11-13

1981 A review of the genus *Dendrobium* section *Callista*. *Orchid Digest,* Vol. 45 (6): 204-210

1981 Some dwarf Dendrobiums. *South African Orchid Journal,* Vol. 12 (3): 80-81

1985 The sections of cultivated species of *Dendrobium*. *South African Orchid Journal*, Vol. 16 (2): 56-59

1985 The Section *Formosae* of the Genus *Dendrobium*. In K.W. Tan (Ed.), *Proceedings of the 11th World Orchid Conference March 1984, Miami*, pp. 308-310

Glossary

The definitions of botanical terms that we have used in the text are given below. They are limited to the sense in which the words have been used in this book. Many of them would have slightly different or broader meanings in a wider botanical context.

acute: sharp pointed

adnate: attached throughout its whole length to another structure of the same kind

anther: the pollen-bearing part of a stamen

anther cap: the outer deciduous cap or case which covers the pollinia

apex: the tip of a leaf, bract, stem or tepal

apical: at the tip

axil: the angle between the upper side of a leaf, branch or bract and the stem, or axis, from which it grows

bract: a small leaf, or leaf-like structure, in the axil of which a flower is borne

callus (sing.) **calli** (pl.): a solid protuberance caused by a mass of cells

canaliculate: channelled, with a longitudinal groove

capsule: a dry fruit that splits open at maturity to release its seeds

ciliate: fringed with short hairs, like eyelashes, on the margin

claw: the narrow, stalk-like base of the petal or lip

column: the central part of the orchid flower, formed by the union of the stamen, style and stigma

connate: when the bases of two opposite parts are joined together

convoluted: when one part is rolled up inside another

cordate: heart shaped

crest: a ridge, usually on one of the tepals, often decorated or fringed

crisped: irregular and curling, usually applied to the margin of a leaf or tepal

deciduous: falling off at some stage in the life of the flower or plant; not evergreen

deflexed: bent or turned sharply downwards

dormant: applied to parts which are not in active growth

dorsal: relating to the back, or outer surface

dorsal sepal: the intermediate, or odd sepal, usually at the back or upper side of the flower

elliptic: shaped like an ellipse, narrowly oblong with regular rounded ends

endemic: confined to a region, or country, and not occurring naturally anywhere else

entire: with an even margin, without teeth or divisions

epiphyte, epiphytic: a plant which grows on other plants but not as a parasite

fimbria (sing.), **fimbriae** (pl.): long thread-like processes which are thicker than hairs

floriferous: producing many flowers

foot: a basal extension of the column

fusiform: spindle shaped, i.e. thickened at the centre and tapering to each end

genus (sing.), **genera** (pl.): the smallest natural group containing distinct species

inflorescence: the arrangement of flowers on the flowering stem

internode: the space or portion of stem between two nodes

keel: a median lengthwise ridge

kciki: a small plant arising from the stem of a mature plant

lateral sepals: the pair of similar sepals arranged at the sides of an orchid flower

lip: the labellum, or odd petal of an orchid flower, usually held on the lower side of the flower, and different in shape, colour and size from the two lateral petals

lithophyte, lithophytic: living on a rock

lobe: a division of an organ, often round but may be of any shape

mentum: a chin-like projection formed at the base of the lip where it joins the column foot or by the united bases of the lateral sepals

meristem: a group of unspecialised cells which are capable of division and becoming specialised to form new tissues of the plant, or a new plant when they have been isolated

moniliform: like a string of beads

node: a point on a stem where a leaf is attached

obcordate: heart shaped, with the widest part at the apex

oblong: much longer than broad, with nearly parallel sides

obovate: reversed ovate, wider at the apical end

orbicular: round and flat

ovary: that part of the flower which contains the ovules; an immature fruit

ovate: egg shaped in outline, usually pointed at the apex, wider towards the base

ovoid: solidly egg shaped

papilla (sing.), **papillae** (pl.): small fleshy protuberance on the surface of the leaf or flower

papillose: bearing papillae

pedicel: the stalk of an individual flower

peduncle: the stalk of an inflorescence

perianth: the colourful parts of the orchid flower, consisting of six tepals which are usually distinguished as three sepals, two petals and the lip

petals: in orchid flowers, two of the three inner members of the perianth, the third is different and is known as the lip

pollinium (sing.), **pollinia** (pl.): a body composed of many pollen grains cohering together

pseudobulb: the thickened stem or stem base of many orchid plants

quadrate: square

raceme: an unbranched inflorescence in which the flowers are borne on short pedicels and usually open in succession from the base upwards

recurved: curved downwards or back upon itself

resupinate: having the lip lowermost because the pedicel or ovary is twisted through 180°

retuse: a rounded end, the centre of which is depressed

rhizome: a root-like stem that creeps under or over the ground or other surface, sending roots downwards and branches, leaves or flowering shoots upwards; always distinguished from a root by the presence of leaves or scales and buds

saccate: pouched or bag shaped

secund: having the flowers arranged apparently in one row along the side of an inflorescence

sepals: the three outermost tepals of the perianth of the flower

sheath: the lower portion of the leaf, clasping the stem; also used for bracts which enclose the flowering stem below those which support the flowers

species: a group of individuals that exhibit the same distinctive characters; the unit which provides the basis for classification

spur: a tubular projection from one of the floral parts, usually the lip

sympodial: a stem made up of a series of superposed branches; each branch terminates in a leaf or flower, and a new branch arises below it to extend the body of the plant

synonym: another name for the same species, genus or section, but one which is no longer in general use

tepal: a division of the perianth; usually used collectively or when the perianth is not markedly differentiated into sepals and petals

terete: cylindrical, circular in cross-section

terrestrial: on or in the ground

tuft, tufted: a group of stems arising very close together from the basal rhizome

undulate: with a wavy margin or surface

variety (var.): a subdivision of a species that is easily recognised by its different size, colour, or other minor modification

velamen: the absorbent epidermis of the roots of many orchids

Index

References to descriptions and illustrations are shown in bold face. References to species mentioned but not illustrated are shown in ordinary type face. Names shown in italics are synonyms.